Comets, Meteoroids, and Asteroids

Mavericks of the Solar System

exploring our universe

Comets, Meteoroids, and Asteroids

Mavericks of the Solar System

by Franklyn M. Branley
Illustrated by Helmut K. Wimmer

THOMAS Y. CROWELL COMPANY   NEW YORK

BY THE AUTHOR

THE CHRISTMAS SKY
EXPERIMENTS IN SKY WATCHING
EXPERIMENTS IN THE PRINCIPLES OF SPACE TRAVEL
EXPLORING BY SATELLITE
MAN IN SPACE TO THE MOON
THE MYSTERY OF STONEHENGE
PIECES OF ANOTHER WORLD: THE STORY OF MOON ROCKS
SOLAR ENERGY

Exploring Our Universe

THE NINE PLANETS
THE MOON: EARTH'S NATURAL SATELLITE
MARS: PLANET NUMBER FOUR
THE SUN: STAR NUMBER ONE
THE EARTH: PLANET NUMBER THREE
THE MILKY WAY: GALAXY NUMBER ONE
COMETS, METEOROIDS, AND ASTEROIDS: MAVERICKS OF
    THE SOLAR SYSTEM

Copyright © 1974 by Franklyn M. Branley
Illustrations copyright © 1974 by Helmut K. Wimmer
All rights reserved. Except for use in a review, the reproduction or utilization of this work in any form or by any electronic, mechanical, or other means, now known or hereafter invented, including xerography, photocopying, and recording, and in any information storage and retrieval system is forbidden without the written permission of the publisher. Published simultaneously in Canada by Fitzhenry & Whiteside Limited, Toronto. Manufactured in the United States of America

Library of Congress Cataloging in Publication Data Branley, Franklyn Mansfield, 1915– Comets, meteoroids, and asteroids: mavericks of the solar system. (Exploring our universe) SUMMARY: Discusses some of the lesser-known astronomical phenomena such as meteorites, asteroids, tektites, zodiacal light, solar wind, and cosmic rays. 1. Solar system—Juv. lit. [1. Solar system] I. Wimmer, Helmut K., illus. II. Title. QB501.3.B7 523.2 73–16043 ISBN 0–690–20176–1

10   9   8   7   6   5   4   3   2   1

For
Tim, David,
Karen, and Susan

Contents

THE METRIC SYSTEM OF MEASUREMENT USES:

meters for length

grams for mass (weight at sea level)

liters for volume

TO CONVERT ENGLISH MEASUREMENTS TO METRIC, OR METRIC TO ENGLISH:

1 inch = 2.54 centimeters	1 centimeter = 0.3937 inch
1 foot = 0.305 meters	1 meter = 39.37 inches
1 yard = 0.914 meters	1 kilometer = 0.621 mile
1 mile = 1.609 kilometers	1 gram = 0.035 ounce
1 pound = 0.454 kilograms	1 kilogram = 2.20 pounds
1 quart = 0.946 liter	1 liter = 1.06 quarts

Comets, Meteoroids, and Asteroids

Mavericks of the Solar System

Meteors and Meteorites │ *1*

The sun, the nine planets going around it, and the thirty-two satellites of these planets are what we usually think of when we consider the solar system. But there are other parts; meteoroids, comets, asteroids, clouds of gas and dust. You might call them strays of the solar system, or mavericks.

While these mavericks do not affect our lives strongly, every once in a while they make their presence known. In 1954, Mrs. Hewlitt Hodges, of Sylacauga, Alabama, became famous because of a maverick. She was napping on her living-room sofa when all of a sudden a 10-pound meteorite (a meteoroid that has reached the earth's surface) crashed through the roof of her house and struck her a bruising blow on her hand and leg. This was the first and only authentic case of a person in the United States being hit by a meteorite. There have been collisions in other parts of the world—in 1511 a monk was killed in Italy along with several birds and sheep when more than a thousand stones fell out of the sky; in 1847, a 40-pound mass of debris fell on a house in Bohemia; in 1911, a dog was hit and killed in Egypt. Records of people and animals and buildings that have been struck are listed in the next two tables.

Reports of Meteorites That Have Struck People and Animals

1500? (B.C.)	"The Lord cast down great stones from Heaven upon them and they died." Joshua 10:11.
616 (A.D.)	China; 10 men were killed, chariots were shattered.
1511	Italy; a fall of more than 1,000 masses killed birds, sheep, and a Franciscan friar.
1794	Italy; a small meteorite fragment pierced a child's hat without harm to the child.
1825	India; a man was killed and a woman injured.
1827	India; a man was struck on the arm.
1836	Brazil; several cattle were killed by a fall of many masses.
1847	Bohemia; 3 children in a bedroom were covered with debris when a 40-pound mass fell through the ceiling.
1860	Ohio; a colt was killed.
1870	India; a man was stunned when a meteorite just missed hitting him.
1911	Egypt; a dog was killed.
1927	Japan; a girl was bruised on the head when hit by a tiny meteorite.
1938	Pennsylvania; a cow was skinned (?).
1946	Mexico; 28 people were injured and several homes destroyed by a fall of many masses.
1953	India; according to a story in the *Atlantic Journal*, a dozen people were killed.
1954	Alabama; a Sylacauga woman was bruised on the thigh when a meteorite fell through the roof.

(The only incident that has been proved is the 1954 one in Sylacauga, Alabama. Meteorite collisions are not usually well documented.)

Meteorites That Have Struck Buildings

1847	19,000 gm	Branau, Bohemia	Penetrated roof and entered bedroom.
1859	11 gm	Bethlehem, New York	Struck side of barn, bounced off, hit a log, bounced again, and rolled into the grass.
1906	999 gm	Constantia, South Africa	Went through 2 thicknesses of corrugated iron and a ceiling.
1911	772 gm	Kilbourn, Wisconsin	Went through about 5 inches of wood roofing and flooring, and then 2½ inches into a clay floor.
1916	611 gm	Baxter, Mississippi	Went through roof, struck a log joist, and remained in attic.
1938	1,770 gm	Benld, Illinois	Went through garage roof, top of car, seat cushion; put dent in muffler.
1938	721 gm	Kasamatsu, Japan	Went through house roof, stopped on floor. Roof was roof tile and wooden roofing, with 1-inch layer of clay between them.
1938	Shower	Pantar, Philippines	16 stones recovered, while thousands of smaller ones fell like rice grains on roofs.
1949	794 gm	Beddgelert, North Wales	Went through 4 thicknesses of slate roofing; shattered wood and ceiling.
1954	3,863 gm	Sylacauga, Alabama	Went through composition roof, ¾-inch decking, ¾-inch ceiling and wallboard; hit a radio.

Meteorites That Have Struck Buildings (Continued)

1968	304 gm	Schenectady, New York	Splintered roof and eaves of a home, bounced to the ground.
1971	368 gm	Wethersfield, Connecticut	Went through house roof and embedded in ceiling.

(1,000 gm = 2.2 lb)

That's one way we are made aware of the presence of one kind of these mavericks. There are many other kinds. We see shooting stars, or comets. Or we see a glow in the night sky that is directly opposite the sun's location. Right now, let's take a look at meteors (the light trails produced when meteoroids enter earth's atmosphere) and meteorites.

In the early morning of November 17, 1966, astronomers and newsmen flew figure eights in a commercial jet 38,000 feet above Nantucket, Massachusetts. They were looking for a repeat display of a Leonid meteor shower which was supposed to be as impressive as the greatest shower of all time—the one that occurred in 1833 when over 10,000 "shooting stars" were seen in one hour.

Altogether, they saw only about 20 meteors. Disappointed, they landed as the sky brightened with the approach of sunrise. That night the astronomers explained the lack of meteors by saying that probably the comet debris related to the shower had been deflected from its orbit by the attraction of Jupiter or Saturn. They did not know that as they were going to sleep (at local sunrise), people in the western part of the country were seeing a magnificent shower of shooting stars. At first, observers in Colorado and Texas saw about 10 meteors a minute. The number increased steadily until 10 new meteors could be seen every second. When the shower reached its peak,

The Leonid shower of 1966 was the most spectacular of this century.

just before and just after 5:00 A.M. Colorado time, which was 7:00 A.M. New York time, some observers believed they saw 1,000 shooting stars in a minute. The sky was filled with streaks of light, and the display was incredible. By six o'clock the activity was only about a hundredth of what it had been at maximum. This shower was a recurrence of the most spectacular display of all time, the one in 1833. That shower had a peak that lasted for 6 hours.

Showers of meteors occur at various times throughout the year on or around the dates shown in the next table. The average number of meteors seen in the past on these dates is indicated.

Major Meteor Showers

SHOWER	DATE OF MAXIMUM ACTIVITY	DURATION (DAYS)* OF VISIBILITY	AVERAGE HOURLY RATE	REMARKS
Quadrantids	January 3	0.5	50	Permanent annual.
Lyrids	April 21	2	10	Permanent annual, associated with Comet 1861 I.
Eta Aquarids	May 4–6	18	20	Permanent annual, possibly associated with Halley's Comet.
Arietids	June 7	20	60	Permanent annual, daytime.
Zeta Perseids	June 9	15	40	Permanent annual, daytime.
Beta Taurids	June 29	10	20	Permanent annual, daytime, associated with Encke's Comet.
Delta Aquarids	July 28	20	20	Permanent annual.
Perseids	August 12	5	50	Permanent annual, associated with Comet 1862 III.
Giacobinids	October 10	0.10	100	Periodic, associated with Comet Giacobini-Zinner (1946 V).
Orionids	October 21	8	20	Permanent annual, possibly associated with Halley's Comet.

Major Meteor Showers (Continued)

SHOWER	DATE OF MAXIMUM ACTIVITY	DURATION (DAYS)* OF VISIBILITY	AVERAGE HOURLY RATE	REMARKS
Taurids	November 3–10	30	10	Permanent annual, associated with Encke's Comet.
Leonids	November 16	4	15	Permanent annual, also periodic (33 years) with greater strength, associated with Comet Tempel-Tuttle (1866 I).
Phoenicids	December 5	0.5	50	Newly discovered (1956), possibly periodic.
Geminids	December 13	6	50	Permanent annual.
Ursids	December 22	2	15	Discovered in 1945, permanent annual, associated with Comet Tuttle (1939 X).

* In which the number of meteors will be ¼ or more of the rate at maximum.

7

The meteor is produced when a small meteoroid, perhaps having little more substance than a small grain of sand, enters the upper atmosphere of the earth and usually vaporizes some 60–70 miles above the earth.

The particle, which might be moving 150,000 miles an hour, collides with molecules in the atmosphere. This heats up the surface of the leading face of the particle, causing bits of it to peel off. The process is called ablation and is precisely the same process that occurs on the leading face of a manned space vehicle during reentry through the atmosphere.

Gases produced by heating of the meteoroid itself and of the air immediately around the object reach temperatures as high as 4,000°F. They radiate the energy in the form of visible light. Incidentally, spectroscopic analysis of this light enables scientists to determine the materials that are contained in the object. The meteor is the mass of glowing gases which sometimes is several hundred yards in diameter, sometimes only a foot or so. It has been computed that a meteoroid (the meteor-producing object) the size of a walnut can produce a meteor (a fast-moving glowing gas cloud) some 1,000 feet across.

METEOR SHOWERS

The particles that produce meteor showers may be material out of which comets are presently forming. Or, as more commonly believed, they may originate in comets. A comet nucleus is little more than frozen gases with bits of solid matter embedded in it. The mass of a comet is small and a comet has a weak gravitational field. When a comet moves in close to the sun or a major planet (especially Jupiter or Saturn) gravitation literally pulls away part of it. Some of the gases of which a comet is composed are torn away, so also are the bits of solid debris contained in the nucleus. The stray solid particles tend to move in the same orbit that the main comet body travels in. After many close approaches, the debris may be spread evenly throughout the orbit. If there have been few such events, there may be regions within the orbit where the debris is more dense.

When the earth moves into this dusty trail, bits of debris move into our atmosphere as explained above, producing a meteor. In any night of the year you should be able to see 10 or 12 meteors in an hour, providing the sky is clear and dark and you pay attention to your observing. If you follow the directions under meteor watching on page 11 you'll probably see many more. On rare occasions an observer will see so many meteors he cannot count them. This was the case with the Leonid Shower of 1966 described earlier.

Sporadic meteors are those which we cannot predict, and which may come from any direction whatsoever. Meteor showers can be predicted for the most part. The meteors in a shower all seem to come from a single location in the sky, called the radiant. A shower usually takes its name from the constellation from which it seems to radiate, either the modern name or an earlier and now obsolete name. Or a shower may take its name from a star or from the comet with which it is associated. So we have the Leonids, that appear to come from the constellation Leo; the Beta Taurids, named for the star Beta in Taurus; and the Bielids, named for Biela's comet. (The suffix *id* is taken from the Greek and means "daughter of.")

Actually, a meteor shower does not radiate from a constellation or a star any more than railroad tracks converge at some distant location, although they seem to. The reason for the apparent motion of meteors in a shower from a common location is shown on page 10. The meteors are moving in parallel lines as shown. The observer sees them as though they radiate from a single location because of the viewing angle.

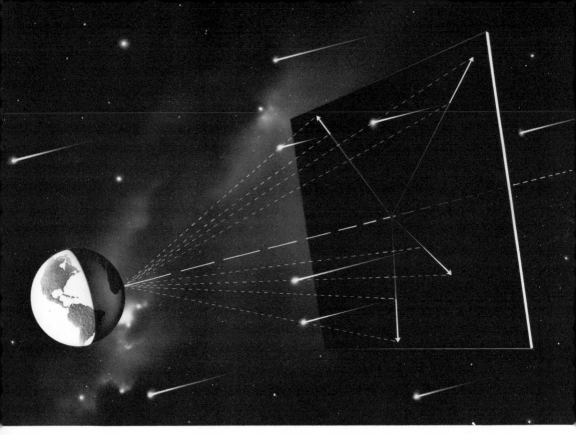

Meteors travel parallel to each other. However, an observer sees sky events two-dimensionally, as though they were displayed on the surface of the celestial sphere. To him meteors appear to radiate (solid arrows) from a point in the sky called the radiant (heavy broken line). (To show the phenomenon clearly we have the events occurring far from earth. Actually meteors appear in earth's atmosphere.)

In addition to those showers that can be observed, there are many showers in which the meteors are too dim for un-aided-eye visibility. Also radar has indicated that numerous showers occur during the daytime when the brightness of the sky prevents our seeing the meteors.

It's difficult to ascertain the amount of meteoric material

that falls upon the earth in a 24-hour period. However, 20,000 tons seems to be not at all unreasonable. Part of this total would be made up of dim and microscopic objects (micrometeorites) and part would be fine ash remaining from those shower particles that do not vaporize completely.

Twenty thousand tons is a significant amount of material. However, it is negligible when compared with the mass of the earth—some 6×10^{21} tons (6,000,000,000,000,000,000,000,000).

METEOR WATCHING

Without consciously looking for them, just about everyone has seen a meteor ("shooting star") at some time. If you were to scan the sky carefully, you should see 10 or more meteors in an hour on any clear night when the sky is dark—no moon to brighten it.

If you were part of a meteor-watching team, your combined score of sightings would be much higher. And, if you were a member of an experienced team during a meteor shower, your score would be very impressive.

Meteors are seen more abundantly after midnight. The earth moves at about 66,000 miles per hour (18.5 miles per second) in its journey around the sun. The velocity of the objects through space is about 26 miles per second (93,600 miles per hour). If the earth were standing still, the objects would move at that speed through our atmosphere. However, between 6:00 P.M. and 12:00 P.M. the earth is moving in the same direction as incoming meteoroids. Therefore, the velocity of the meteors is 7 or 8 miles per second (the difference between 26 miles per second and 18 miles per second). From midnight to dawn, the earth may be moving toward meteoroids which are

Because of earth's annual motion, an observer before midnight moves in the same direction as any meteoroids that might enter the atmosphere. After midnight and toward morning, the best time for observing, he moves toward the meteoroids.

also moving toward the earth. Therefore, their velocity is some 44 miles per second (the sum of 26 miles per second and 18 miles per second). The high-velocity meteoroids are brighter than those moving at slower speeds and more can be seen when the earth is running into them, so the best time to observe meteors is after midnight and into early morning.

Plan to watch with someone else. Two persons are better than one, and four are better than two. Use reclining lawn chairs, and select a location where the sky is not obscured by trees and buildings. Dress in warm clothing, and since you might fall asleep, have an alarm clock handy. Arrange your lawn chairs so each person sees one half of the sky if there are two of you, one quarter if there are four persons.

When you are all reclining, do not stare at the entire sky, but scan your area. Shift your gaze from time to time. In this way you will see your entire segment more clearly, rather than only a limited part of it.

When you see the flash of a meteor, mentally retrace its path. If you know the stars and constellations, note those through which it passes, and also trace the line backward to determine the radiant—the area of the sky from which the meteor seemed to be moving.

During a shower, you'll very likely find that most of the meteors appear to come from a particular section of the sky—a particular constellation such as Leo (the Leonids) or Perseus (the Perseids). At other times there will be no pattern to the meteors; there will be no radiant. These are the sporadic meteors.

Meteor watching becomes more interesting when you can relate the light streaks to particular star groups. To do this, study the stars while you are reclining in your meteor-watching chair. Cover a flashlight with red cloth or plastic and use this red light to look at a star map. If you use a clear flashlight, the light is too bright and also the white light causes the pupils of your eyes to close somewhat. Then when you look at the stars you will not see them clearly. The white light reduces dark adaptation—the widening of your pupils to admit more light.

Once you begin to know the stars, you'll learn each one's magnitude, which corresponds to its brightness. A brightness, or magnitude, scale is usually printed somewhere on the star map. When you see a meteor, compare its brightness with that of some nearby star. Then when you record information about the meteor, you can include whether it was magnitude 2, or 3, or whatever.

Some meteors flare up to increased brightness somewhere along the path. If this happens, record the event. You might say

Occasionally meteors are so bright that they illuminate the countryside as they streak across the sky.

the meteor was magnitude 2, but flared momentarily to magnitude 1.5.

Color is another important detail about a meteor. So, if any color is apparent be sure to note that. Also, meteors sometimes develop a train. Gases left by the meteoroid continue to glow, sometimes for a fraction of a second, but sometimes for a minute or longer. You should notice this: how long did the train last? how did it change, if at all? and how long was it? (Length is given in degrees. For measuring, a convenient yardstick to use is the distance between the pointer stars of the Big Dipper, which is 5 degrees, or the diameter of the full moon, which is ½ degree.)

The time of the event should be given as accurately as possible. Before starting an observing period, check your watch against a reliable time signal. If possible, give the time to the nearest second.

Beginning and ending can be given in right ascension and declination if you are using a star chart and if you are familiar with the system. If not, you might divide the sky into four segments—northeast, southeast, southwest, northwest. You can give a rough idea of altitude by remembering it is 90 degrees from the horizon to the zenith—the point of the sky that is directly over your head.

Meteor Record

Date	Sky Conditions	Name of Shower	or Sporadic	Location

NO.	TIME	TRAIN DURATION (SECONDS)	MAGNI- TUDE	CONSTEL- LATION (RADIANT)	BEGIN (DIREC- TION)	END (ALTI- TUDE)	REMARKS
1							
2							
3							
4							
5							

In recording your observations of meteors give the information called for in the sample form on page 15. Be sure to use the remarks column. Here you should mention if the meteor showed any distinctive color. If it flared at all be sure to mention that. Occasionally, a meteor is so bright that it is called by a special name—a fireball. If there is a crackling or popping sound associated with the fireball, it is called a bolide—after a Greek word meaning "missile." Three or four thousand fireball-bolides probably occur every day, although most of them appear over oceans or other uninhabited areas (or in the daytime) and so are not recorded.

Often there isn't time enough to record all this information, and while writing you can miss other meteors. The better approach is to speak the information into a portable tape recorder. Later on, the data can be put on your permanent record sheet. The sheets should be kept in a notebook. You may wish to send copies of them to the American Meteor Society. The address is c/o Dr. David Meisel, Department of Physics and Astronomy, State University College, Geneseo, N.Y. 14454. Serious meteor observers should write to Dr. Meisel to purchase official report forms.

If you're a photography buff, you may wish to photograph meteors, as well as record information about them. To do so you need a camera with a time exposure adjustment on it.

You must have a sky without a glow in it. That is, you must be removed from city lights and the lights of advertising displays. Set the camera on a firm support so it will not wiggle. Aim at the dark sky (in the general direction of the source of a shower if a shower is expected) and open the shutter for about one half hour. The camera should be f 4.5 or thereabouts and loaded with fast film. (Exposure times and film cannot be given precisely. The best procedure is to experiment until you find the right combination for your particular conditions.)

To be sure you do not blur your film if you should budge the camera, hold a card in front of the lens while you are opening it. Similarly, when ending the exposure, hold the card in front of the lens and then close it. Note the time of opening and closing the lens. Move to the next frame and continue the operations.

Long exposures such as these suggested will cause the stars to appear as streaks on your photographs. However, even if you are familiar with the constellations, you may have difficulty recognizing them on your photographs. To do so, cover the photograph with a piece of tracing paper and mark the beginning of each star trail or the end of it. On the paper you will see the star pattern which produced the streaks.

Sometime you may be lucky enough to photograph a rich meteor shower. If so, expose your film long enough to pick up 10 or so meteors. Should the frequency increase, expose your film for shorter and shorter periods—perhaps only fifteen seconds for each frame. Be sure to record the time each exposure was made. Later on, then, you can plot the number of meteors against time, giving you a graph of shower activity. Such information is of value to professional astronomers.

METEORITES

When a meteoroid is large enough to penetrate our atmosphere and reach earth's surface, it is called a meteorite. Similarly, particles that fall on the moon or other planets are also called meteorites.

Throughout history, and long before history was written, meteors and meteorites were associated with the gods. A meteor was a sign that a chieftain or prince had died, or would die in the near future. A fireball was cause for deep concern for it was thought to be an expression of the anger of the gods with the people or a warning of a calamity, just as was the appearance of a comet.

As for meteorites, "the stones that fell from the sky," for many years scientists thought such an idea preposterous. Admittedly, there were many reports that people had actually seen these "stones" fall to the earth but no scientist had. That is, not until 1794 when a German physicist, Ernst Chladni, wrote a paper suggesting that stones and metals he had seen had come from outside the earth. Later, the scientist Jean Baptiste Biot was commissioned by the French Academy to report on a fall that had occurred in the city of L'Aigle in broad daylight on April 26, 1803. He investigated the fall himself and questioned witnesses who had seen a bright exploding meteor just previous to the fall of meteorites. The stones, still smoking, fell over an area of some seven miles. The largest object, of some 2,000 that were recovered, weighed 22 pounds.

That report marked the beginning of serious study of meteorites. The number that fall upon the earth is not known, but the total amount must be very large. While large meteorites are rare—those over 10 tons are listed on page 30—small ones the size of acorns, grains of sand, and even smaller that fall on the earth in 24 hours may, as we have noted, add up to 20,000 tons or so.

Small meteorites may be the debris of a comet. This is certainly true for micrometeorites, those so small a microscope is needed to see them, and even larger meteorites may have the same origin. Still larger meteorites, and surely those that are measured in tons, appear to be mavericks of the asteroid belt.

The region between the orbits of Mars and Jupiter contains some 1,500 asteroids that have been identified and whose orbits have been plotted. There probably are additional thousands to be discovered. It is possible that the orbits of asteroids are disturbed by the gravitational fields of Saturn or Jupiter to such an extent that asteroids move toward the earth. These asteroids, if such they be, have been bombarding the earth for millions of years. Occasionally one of them is found, and invariably exciting stories are associated with the discovery. So it was with Ahnighito.

The Ahnighito

In 1818 the British explorer Captain John Ross met a tribe of Cape York Eskimos while on an Arctic expedition. He noticed that some of the Eskimos had knives and harpoons made of iron imbedded in bone handles. Captain Ross inquired of the Eskimos about the iron knives and other tools made of iron. He was curious, for he knew that Eskimos did not dig iron ore and smelt it to obtain pure metal.

The Eskimos told him of an iron mountain—a mountain where there were the Saviksue, the Great Irons. Sir John's expedition was unable to find the place. However, stories of the Saviksue persisted. Whenever polar explorers assembled, talk always came around to the Greenland Eskimos and their iron implements.

For almost a hundred years the mystery remained unsolved. The solution started to unfold in 1893 when Robert E. Peary set out on a polar expedition, one purpose of which was to locate the Great Irons. He gained the friendship of the Eskimos, and one named Tallkoteah guided Peary to the site of the Saviksue. Small meteorites were scattered about, but there were two in the area that must have caused Peary great excitement. It took a year of digging to free the meteorites from the rock and soil packed around them.

In 1894 Peary's ship, the *Falcon,* returned to the United

States with Peary's wife and daughter. Peary himself chose to spend the winter in Greenland. After discharging its passengers at Philadelphia, the *Falcon* set out for Greenland again. On the way it foundered and was lost with all hands. The next year, through the efforts of Mrs. Peary and with the help of the American Museum of Natural History, another ship, the *Kite*, was obtained. It went north in 1895 to seek out the meteorites once again and to meet with Peary.

The *Kite* set out for Cape York to collect the meteorites that had been located earlier. The smallest of the meteorites was called the Dog. It weighs about a ton and so could be loaded aboard the ship without too much difficulty. A larger one, called the Woman, was quite another problem. When Peary saw it, this meteorite was the same size and shape as it now is in its permanent resting place at the American Museum –Hayden Planetarium. Originally, however, the meteorite was perhaps larger. For as long as they could remember Eskimos had been removing pieces of iron from this Saviksue. The metal is relatively soft, and it is malleable—it can be shaped by pounding. The pieces were beaten into metal blades for knives and other tools. The remaining part of the Woman weighs about 3 tons, so it had to be lifted by jacks onto timbers and then dragged over rollers that rested on planks. The planks were laid along a crude roadway that ran from the hillside, where the meteorite was found, to the water's edge. The iron was put upon a large cake of ice and floated out to the ship.

The largest meteorite—called Ahnighito (the tent) by the Eskimos—was some seven miles away from the Dog and the Woman. That year Peary could not attempt to budge it. Winter winds were blowing, new ice was forming, and the *Kite* had to leave before ice crushed it.

In 1896 Peary returned to Greenland with a heavier ship,

the *Hope,* and powerful jacks, heavy timbers and lines—massive equipment to perform a massive task, the transporting of the meteorite (the Iron Mountain, as some Eskimos called it) to the water's edge. It was a dense mass twice as long as a man, some 6 feet high and 5 feet across, and was later found to weigh just 85 pounds more than 34 tons. After weeks of digging, jacking, pushing, sliding, and dragging, the tremendous meteorite was at the water's edge. Once at waterside, Ahnighito was jacked up and heavy timbers were slid under it. Ahnighito was ready for loading aboard the *Hope.* But the cruel winter was only days away, and the ship had to get away from the deadly new ice that was forming rapidly.

It wasn't until one year later that the meteorite was on board ship and on its long journey to New York City. In 1897 the *Hope* once more anchored at Cape York. A heavy bridge was built from the shore to the ship. Two of the oak timbers used for the bridge were 12 × 16 inches and 60 feet long—seasoned and straight grained. Each timber weighed three tons. Heavy flooring was built in the deck of the ship and super heavy supports in the hold where Ahnighito would be placed.

When all was ready, and the tide was right, Marie Ahnighito Peary, the four-year-old daughter of Robert and Josephine Peary, broke a small bottle of wine over the meteorite and christened it Ahnighito, the name the Eskimos had given it long, long ago. The winches were started, and slowly Ahnighito was inched aboard the *Hope.*

On October 2, 1897, a hundred-ton crane at the Brooklyn Navy Yard lifted Ahnighito from the *Hope* onto a dock. For seven years the meteorite lay there and then it was moved to the American Museum of Natural History. In 1935 Ahnighito was transferred to the Hayden Planetarium, where it is on permanent display.

THE AHNIGHITO METEORITE

1. Ahnighito, imbedded in the ground, was a curiosity to the Eskimos of Cape York, Greenland.

2. The meteorite was dug out and mounted on timbers to be moved inch by inch to the shore.

3. Ahnighito was slid slowly on heavy timbers from the shore to the deck of the *Hope*.

4. Ice that came with the approach of the long winter was a constant hazard in transporting Ahnighito.

5. At the turn of the century Ahnighito was moved from the Brooklyn Navy Yard to The American Museum of Natural History.

6. In its present location at the Hayden Planetarium, Ahnighito tips the scale at 68,085 pounds.

Siberia Tunguska 1908

When a meteorite strikes the solid earth, you would expect it to make a crater. But there were no craters associated with the Cape York Meteorites. They were embedded in the ground, but not deeply. Some people believe that the meteorites fell into ice that blanketed that part of the world some thousands of years ago—perhaps during the Pleistocene, or glacial, epoch. As the ice melted, the irons settled into solid ground.

One more exciting incident in the story of meteors and meteorites occurred in Siberia in 1908. It is another case of a meteorite, or perhaps a comet, colliding with the earth yet leaving no crater of the usual kind.

At six o'clock in the morning of June 30, 1908, a Trans-Siberian train was passing through Kansk, Siberia. Passengers aboard the train saw a fireball brighter, larger, more awesome than any witnessed by modern man. It passed from south to north. A few seconds later there were explosive, thunderous sounds. The train came to a screeching stop, the engineer fearing that some part of his train had exploded, or that it might be blown from the tracks.

A peasant, S. B. Semenoc, who lived on the Podkamennaya Tunguska about forty miles away from the center of the explosion, had this to say:

> I sat on my open porch, with my face toward the north, and at that time there arose, in a moment, a conflagration which gave off such heat that it was impossible to remain sitting—it almost burned the shirt off me. And it was such a flaming wonder that I noticed it occupied a space of not less than two versts [about a mile and a quarter]. But to make up for that, the conflagration endured only a very short time: I had time only to cast my eyes in that direction to see how large it was when in a moment it vanished. After

this vanishing, it grew dark and at the same time there was an explosion which threw me off the open porch about seven feet or more; but I did not remain unconscious very long; I came to myself and there was such a crashing sound that all the houses shook and seemed to move from their foundations. It broke the window panes and window frames in the houses, and in the center of the square near the huts, a strip of earth was torn out.

Another witness, who was only one mile from the center of the explosion, was deafened by the sound. In a single moment his herd of fifteen hundred reindeer disappeared, except for a few charred carcasses.

Effects of the fall were felt or seen for hundreds of miles around the area. Sounds were heard 900 miles away, earth vibrations were recorded 3,000 miles away, pressure waves in the air were felt everywhere. People 500 miles away saw the flash of light, and the great column of fire that rose above the region could be seen some 300 miles away.

This event in 1908 has been called the Tunguska. Some twenty years later the area was studied by Russian scientists. They found about 100 craters ranging in size from 25 to 100 feet across. But they did not appear to be meteorite craters. No meteorites—either large or small—were found in the area. Perhaps the object was not a meteorite but the core of a small comet, one having a mass of some 40,000 tons. It could have collided at high velocity, causing instantaneous generation of tremendous heat and explosive pressure. Any "ice" chips which may have survived the explosion would, of course, have melted before anyone arrived on the scene. Such a possibility might account for the various sights and sounds that were produced.

When the region was explored by scientists they found that all the trees in a region 40 miles across had been blown down, the tops pointed away from the center. The entire region was one of devastation.

It has been suggested that the Tunguska event might have been a "black hole" passing through the earth. This would be a small object, perhaps no larger than a grain of sand but weighing a million billion tons and moving some 25,000 miles per hour. Gravitation is so great in such a mass that nothing can escape, not even light, to reveal its presence. Thus the name black hole. Shock waves generated by such an impact would have been great enough to have caused the felling of trees, the bright illumination, and the tremendous boom. When the black hole emerged from the earth, a similar shock wave would have been produced, perhaps in the North Atlantic. Evidence of such a wave is being sought by some investigators.

The cause of the Tunguska event is still a mystery. Maybe it was the result of a black hole penetrating the earth, or a meteorite of antimatter that exploded in the atmosphere, or a nuclear device sent to earth by an extraterrestrial civilization. Such theories have been suggested. However, the comet-impact theory has the widest support.

Sikhote-Alin 1947

Another fall occurred in Russia in 1947, near the Sikhote-Alin Mountains. People reported that the meteor was as bright as the sun. After impact, a column of dust rose some 25 miles high.

When Soviet scientists arrived they found 106 craters, some of them 100 feet across. The trees around the main craters were felled, and all lay with their tops away from the craters. Other large trees were pulled out of the ground by the roots and piled one atop the other like straws.

Estimates of the size of the meteorite run as high as 200 tons. However, the largest chunk recovered is about 700 pounds. It is believed that the meteorite shattered before it

struck the earth. Several tons of meteoritic iron have been recovered from the area, most of it in very small pieces.

The Canyon Diablo Meteorite

A true meteorite crater, and perhaps the most famous in the world, is located near Winslow, Arizona. It is named the Winslow Crater, or the Canyon Diablo Crater after the meteorite that produced it. Canyon Diablo is the name of the nearest post office, and traditionally the nearest post office becomes the name of newfound meteorites.

The crater is gigantic—4,000 feet across and 570 feet deep—and in places the rim of the crater is raised almost 100 feet above the level of the plateau.

It is believed that about 20,000 years ago a meteoritic mass some 40 feet across and weighing at least 50,000 tons (some people say 2 million tons) came crashing into the earth at nearly 15 miles per second. The heat generated was more than enough to shatter the meteorite and gouge out the crater.

Daniel Morreau Barringer, a mining engineer, was convinced that the meteorite did not shatter but buried itself beneath the floor of the crater. He bought the crater and sank a shaft, hoping to find a source of rich iron. The drill did strike some iron but not rich enough for Barringer to pursue the venture. How much nickel-iron lies below the floor of the crater is still unknown. However, nickel-iron fragments have been found all around the area. The largest one weighs 1,406 pounds. Some 2,000 tons of debris in the form of weathered rock and iron can be accounted for.

Kinds of Meteorites

Meteorites may be classified into three main groups. The first group is the irons, or siderites. These are mixtures of many metals, but iron usually makes up 90 or 95 percent of the total, and nickel may run from 5 to 10 percent.

The second group is the siderolites, made of stony iron. They are very rare. Perhaps this is because the stony part decomposes more rapidly than the metal. After a prolonged period only the metal remains.

The third group is the aerolites, or stones, which are made mostly of silicates. The stones also contain iron and nickel, though the amount does not exceed 10 or 15 percent.

The most common meteorites that fall are stones, but the most common meteorites in collections are irons. This sounds contradictory, but it isn't. When meteorites are seen to fall and are recovered, more than 90 percent of them are stones. However, when a meteorite whose fall has not been observed is found, in most cases it will be an iron.

Stony meteorites do not weather well. They break down chemically and mechanically. Also, aerolites look very much like terrestrial rocks, so one passes right over them. Even experts often have difficulty identifying the stony meteorites— they do so by careful study of the iron and nickel they contain. Irons are rare too, especially in those countries that have been using iron tools for centuries. A person finding an iron would be lucky, for the metal could have been shaped into tools. Most iron meteorites display Widmanstaetten figures, named for A. B. Widmanstaetten, a Viennese scientist who first described them in 1808. When a face of the iron is cut, polished, and then etched with acid, the structure of the metal is revealed as shown in the drawing. Heating of the irons followed by slow cooling during their stay in deep outer space (a degree in a million years) apparently caused the crystals to line up in this curious fashion.

All the recovered meteorites—siderites, siderolites, and aerolites—are apparently associated with sporadic meteors, those which cannot be predicted. As far as we know the particles in meteor showers are not massive enough to become meteorites, that is, to penetrate the atmosphere. However, when the light of a meteor shower is studied, we find strong indication that the material producing them is stony in nature.

In four or five instances, investigators have found small diamonds inside meteorites. The diamonds are very small, black, and opaque, quite unlike jewel diamonds. In order for diamonds to form, graphite must be subjected to severe pressure. Early investigators suggested that the pressure was exerted inside a mass of material about the size of the moon. Perhaps meteorites came from such a body. However, careful study of meteorites, especially of the Widmanstaetten patterns mentioned above, indicated that the meteorites had cooled

One positive identification of certain types of meteorite is the Widmanstaetten lines or figures, crystallization that results from extremely slow cooling.

slowly from 700° to 400°. This immediately disproved the theory that meteorites come from a moon-sized body, because a body that size would not have cooled to 700°, let alone 400°, in the entire history of the solar system.

It is now generally believed that tremendous shock waves were set up in the Canyon Diablo Meteorite (one that has diamonds in some 120 of the fragments) as it crashed into the earth. This would have produced the pressure required for diamonds to be created. In other cases it is believed that diamonds may have resulted when asteroids collided in space, or exploded after such a collision.

The Largest Meteorite Finds, Each Over 10 Tons

Hoba West	Grootfontein, Bechuanaland, S.W. Africa; estimated 60 tons, 1 mass.
Ahnighito	Cape York, Greenland; 34 tons. Found along with the Woman, 3 tons, the Dog, 900 pounds, and Savik, 3½ tons.
Bacubirito	Senaloa, Mexico; estimated at 30 tons, 1 mass.
Santa Catharina	Brazil; estimated at 25 tons, several masses.
Chupaderos	Chihuahua, Mexico; 23 tons, 2 masses.
Xiquipilco	Ixtlahuaca, Mexico; estimated at 20 to 25 tons, many masses.
Meteor Crater (Canyon Diablo)	Arizona; estimated at 20 tons to 2,000 tons, many masses.
Bethany	Great Namaqualand, South Africa; 16.5 tons, 51 masses.
Willamette	Willamette Valley, Oregon; 14 tons.
El Morito	Chihuahua, Mexico; 11 tons, 1 mass.

Sources of Meteorites

Asteroids go around the sun in the region between Mars and Jupiter. Perhaps meteorites have their origin there. Meteorites are among the oldest objects we know of—dating back some 4.6 billion years, to the beginning of the solar system. In the case of the Canyon Diablo Meteorite, its parent body, perhaps an asteroid, became very hot some 4½ billion years ago and melted, separating the iron and nickel from the stony material. During the next billion years or so the mass cooled slowly, producing the Widmanstaetten pattern we now find. In the temperature range from 700° to 400°, the cooling occurred at the rate of 1° in a million years. Scientists would expect such a cooling rate in an asteroid 200 to 400 miles in diameter.

Later, collision with other asteroids, or comets may have broken them apart and knocked them into new orbits, or orbits may have been altered by the attraction of planets or other asteroids. In any event, the orbits were changed enough for the mass to intercept earth's orbit.

Asteroids play an important part in the story of meteorites. They are part of our solar system, so it's proper that we should take a closer look at them.

In the night sky asteroids appear as points of light, not unlike stars, and so they are given the name *asteroid,* after *aster,* the Latin word for "star." *Asteroid* means "starlike."

A list of asteroids sounds like the roster of a girls' academy —Iris, Flora, Victoria, Irene, Eleanora, Eva, and Daphne. Or, it might sound like a roll of characters from mythology—Ceres, Pallas, Juno.

A person who discovers an asteroid has the privilege of naming it. Depending upon their interests, discoverers have named asteroids after legendary heroines, flowers, or cities. Some are named for governors and presidents, and so we have the asteroids Hooveria, Rockefellia, and Washingtonia.

Johann Titius first expressed the distance relationships of the planets, which later became the Titius-Bode Law.

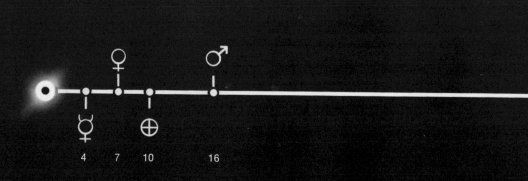

The first asteroid discovered was named Ceres, after the Roman goddess of vegetation and the goddess that protected the island of Sicily. At first the asteroid was called Ceres Ferdinandia in honor of King Ferdinand IV of Naples and Sicily.

In the latter part of the eighteenth century, astronomers were concerned about the way planets were distributed in the solar system. Study of the planets and their motions led people to suspect there might be another undiscovered planet. The idea was first recorded in 1741 in a book written by Christian von Wolff. About ten years later Johann David Titius (1729–1796) published a careful study of the relationship of the distances of planets from the sun. In part Titius wrote:

> Take heed of the distances of the planets from each other and note that in almost every case they are separated from each other in proportion to their increase in size. If the distance from the sun to Saturn is reckoned as 100 parts, then Mercury is 4 such parts away from the sun; Venus is $4 + 3 = 7$ thereof, Earth $4 + 6 = 10$; Mars $4 + 12 = 16$. But now notice that from Mars to Jupiter there is a deviation of this exact proportion. From Mars there follows a space of $4 + 24 = 28$ such parts in which to date no main planet or satellite has been observed.

Titius went on to suggest that there were moons of Mars in

52   100

that space or moons of Jupiter. One of the men who read of Titius' theory was Johann Elert Bode (1747–1826), who was director of the Berlin Observatory. Bode believed Titius was correct, and Bode spread the word, encouraging observers to look in the region between Mars and Jupiter for bodies so far undiscovered. Bode was quite sure there was a planet in that space, not satellites of Mars and Jupiter.

The relationship between the planets is now called Bode's Law (or more accurately the Titius-Bode Law). Actually, the system that Titius worked out is more of a relationship than a law. It breaks down for the outer planets, as you can see in the table below. However, it is remarkably accurate for the planets out to Uranus.

Bode's Law works this way. Write out the numbers 0, 3, 6, 12, 24, 48 and so on until you reach 768. Add 4 to each number. Take $\frac{1}{10}$ of each result. This will be the distances to the planets in astronomical units (AU). The distance between the earth and the sun, 93 million miles, is 1 astronomical unit.

Bode's "Law"

PLANET		ONE-TENTH	ACTUAL DIST. (AU)
Mercury	0 plus 4	.4	0.39
Venus	3 plus 4	.7	0.72
Earth	6 plus 4	1.0	1.00
Mars	12 plus 4	1.6	1.52
Asteroids	24 plus 4	2.8	1.46 to 5.71
Jupiter	48 plus 4	5.2	5.20
Saturn	96 plus 4	10.0	9.54
Uranus	192 plus 4	19.6	19.18
Neptune	384 plus 4	38.8	30.06
Pluto	768 plus 4	77.2	39.52

But the fact that the "law" does not hold throughout the solar system is not important for our purposes. In the story of asteroids the "law" provided observers with a place to explore, and that is exactly what they did.

In 1796 delegates to a meeting of astronomers decided they would search the region between Mars and Jupiter. Each selected a section of the sky to observe with care. But the discovery of the first asteroid was not made by any of the delegates. Piazzi, an Italian astronomer, is credited with making the discovery.

Giuseppe Piazzi (1746–1826), director of an observatory on the island of Sicily, was involved in correcting a star catalog. Catalogs list the positions of stars and give information about them. The catalogs must be accurate so that astronomers can locate any particular star for further study. Piazzi had found errors in the catalog he was checking, and on this particular night he was observing the area of Taurus.

On January 1, 1801, the first night of the nineteenth century, Piazzi saw a star he had never seen before, and one that was not cataloged. The next night he saw it again. It had moved and so he knew it could not be a star. Piazzi thought he had discovered a comet, but his colleague Bode convinced Piazzi he had found the long-lost planet—the one between Mars and Jupiter.

Piazzi became ill before he could complete his observations of the elusive "planet." When he recovered and looked once more, the object could not be found. No orbit had been worked out for it, and so other observers could not find the "planet" either. It appeared that Piazzi would not receive credit for the discovery. Fortunately Karl Friedrich Gauss (1777–1855), whose name is given to the unit of magnetic force, was able to determine the orbit of Piazzi's "planet." For several months the object was too close to the sun to be observed. But just one year after the discovery other astronomers, following the directions Gauss had given, found the object as predicted and gave it the name of Ceres.

Shortly after the first asteroid was discovered, an amateur astronomer named Wilhelm Olbers found asteroid number two. His asteroid, found on March 28, 1802, was called Pallas, for the goddess of wisdom. Could there be several "planets" out there, besides these two occupants of the space between Mars and Jupiter? Many wondered about the possibility and explored the area with their telescopes. Then, in 1804, asteroid number three was discovered. Karl Harding, who found it, named the asteroid for Juno, queen of the gods. Three years later Wilhelm Olbers found another one. Asteroid number four was called Vesta, after the Roman goddess of the hearth.

These four asteroids—Ceres, Pallas, Juno, and Vesta—turn out to be the four largest, and also the brightest. It is understandable why they were the first to be discovered.

NAME	DIAMETER (MILES)	BRIGHTNESS (MAGNITUDE)
Ceres	478.5	7.4
Pallas	304.5	8.0
Juno	118	8.7
Vesta	236	6.5

Stars and other celestial objects must be magnitude 6 or brighter to be seen without a telescope. With binoculars, one can pick out magnitude 10 objects under clear skies. In the magnitude scale brightness increases as the magnitude number decreases. For example, the magnitude of the sun is −26; the brightest stars are magnitude −1, the dimmest stars we can see are magnitude +6; and the photographic limit of the 200–inch telescope on Mt. Palomar is +23.5. Those asteroids that come closest to the earth are shown below:

Asteroids Closest to Earth

ASTEROID	DISCOVERER AND YEAR	CLOSEST APPROACH (MILES)	PERIOD (YEARS)	DIAM- ETER (MILES)
Eros	Charlois and Witt, 1898	13,900,000	1.76	20
Amor	Delporte, 1932	10,400,000	2.67	1.5
Geographos	Wilson and Minkowski, 1951	5,600,000	1.39	2.0
Icarus	Baade, 1949	4,000,000	1.12	0.8
Apollo	Reinmuth, 1932	2,500,000	1.81	1.0
Adonis	Delporte, 1936	1,200,000	2.76	1.0
Hermes	Reinmuth, 1937	475,000	2.00	0.75

After the discovery of Vesta came a period of some forty years without any discoveries. But by the end of the nineteenth century, photography had made it much easier to identify asteroids. They make streaks of light in photographs of star fields. Today some 1,600 asteroids have been identified. We know their orbits and can predict where they will be in the future. But this number does not begin to tell the story. Most asteroids are very small and so dim that even the largest telescope cannot find them. Some people believe that there are 40,000 to 50,000 asteroids within the range of the 100-inch telescope, an instrument that can photograph objects down to magnitude +21.

If there are 50,000 undiscovered asteroids, as has been suggested, most of them would be very small, only a few yards across or less. The mass of the 1,600-odd asteroids we know about would altogether equal only about ⅛₄₇, and some say ⅟₁₆₀₀, of the mass of the earth. Were all the asteroids to be melted together and formed into a globe, its diameter would be less than 500 miles. The earth, you recall, is 8,000 miles in diameter.

It would seem that Titius and Bode were not correct about a planet existing between Mars and Jupiter. A globe 500 miles across would not make a very impressive satellite, let alone a planet. Nevertheless, Wilhelm Olbers suggested that the asteroids were the remnants of a planet that had been shattered by some explosive catastrophe. He believed that the asteroids returned to the same region of the sky sometime during an orbit, indicating they all had a common origin. However, they do not return to the identical area. So the theory is weakened, according to some observers. Not so, say others; it merely shows that the orbits of some of the asteroids are perturbed by major planets.

Today the more popular theory suggests that the asteroids and the planets were formed at about the same time and from the same materials, or they are the products of collisions between bodies considerably smaller than planets but which formed when planets evolved. The main support of this argument is observations of the orbits of asteroids. They seem to fall into similar groups, or families, as would be expected if the asteroids were debris remaining after collisions.

If meteoroids are actually stray asteroids, as many believe, the argument for a similar origin for planets and asteroids is strengthened. Meteorites and probably all meteoroids contain the same materials as those contained in the earth itself. And the age of meteorites (4.6 billion years) turns out to be very similar to what is believed to be the age of the earth. When you see a meteorite (the Ahnighito, for example) it's awesome to think that it may have been an asteroid—an object that for billions of years was in orbit far beyond Mars.

While the asteroids occur in the region between the orbits of Mars and Jupiter, they are not distributed evenly throughout that region. There are regions where no asteroids have been found. They are called the Kirkwood gaps, after Daniel

The orbit of Icarus passes within 17 million miles of the sun, closer than Mercury. At its greatest distance (apogee) Icarus is 183 million miles from the sun, inside the orbit of Mars. Every nineteen years Icarus and earth are separated by only 4 million miles. The asteroid has a period of 1.1 years.

At the ascending node (Ω) the plane of the orbit of Icarus rises above the plane of the solar system; at the descending node ($\mho$) it moves below.

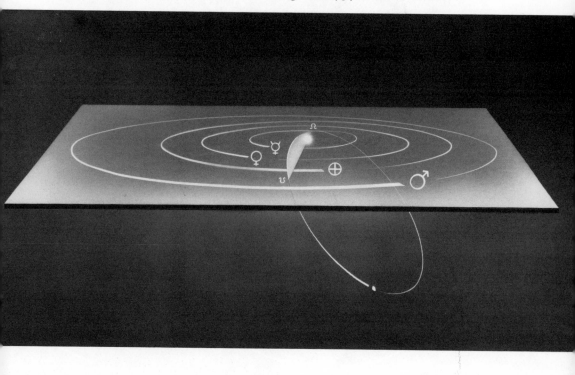

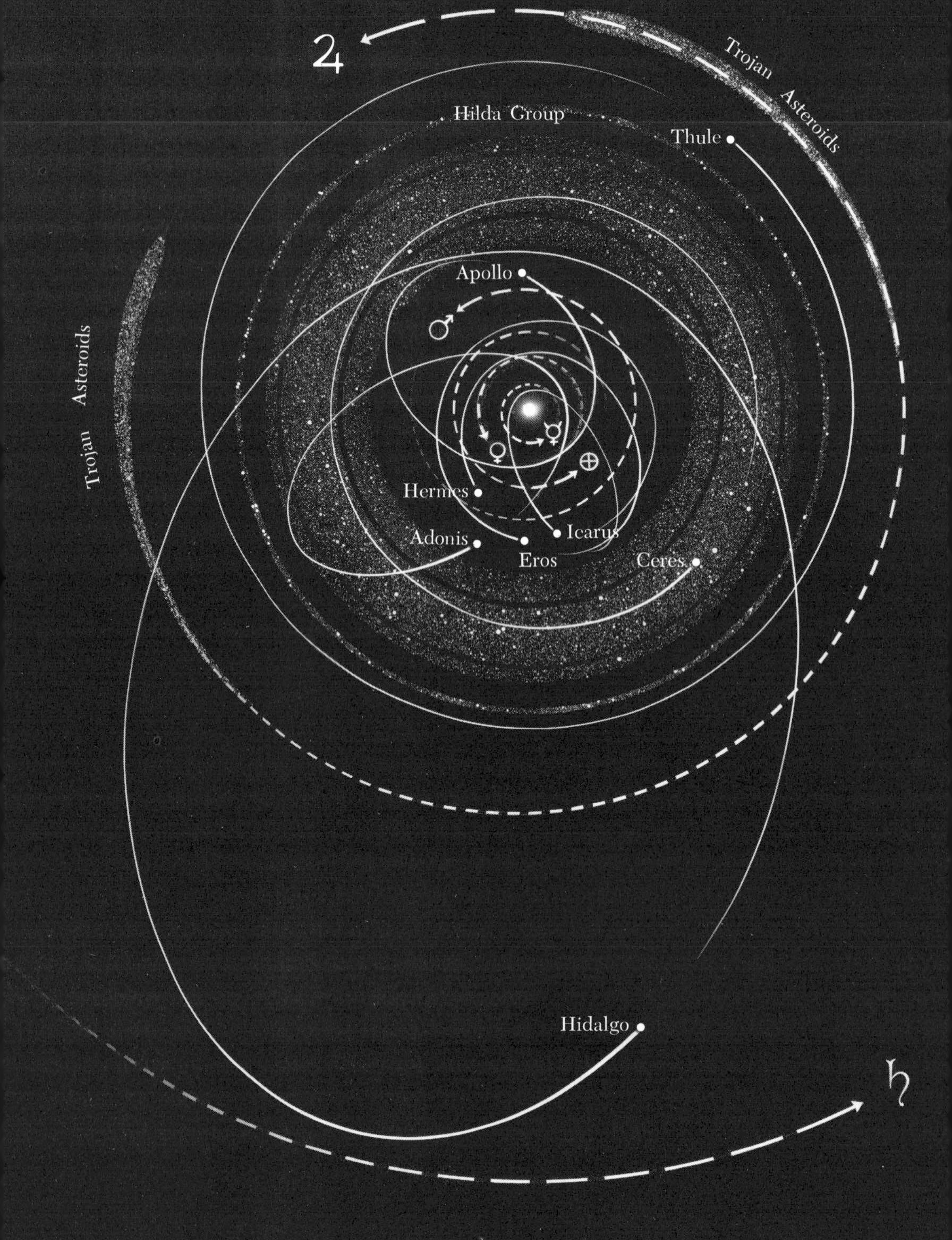

2

Trojan Asteroids

Hilda Group

Thule •

Trojan Asteroids

Apollo •

♂

Hermes •

Adonis •

Icarus •

Eros •

Ceres •

Hidalgo •

♄

Kirkwood, who first explained them. The gaps correspond to simple fractions of the time it takes Jupiter to go around the sun, which means that at regular intervals the asteroids would be close to Jupiter. For example, an asteroid ⅝ Jupiter's distance from the sun would have a period of revolution ½ that of Jupiter's. Therefore, every time two orbits were completed, the asteroid would be close to Jupiter. The regular attraction of Jupiter would eventually pull the asteroid out of the orbit, leaving a gap.

There is a group of asteroids that moves in the same orbit that Jupiter follows. They are called the Trojans. In 1772 Joseph Louis Lagrange (1736–1813), a French mathematician, theorized that there are two points in Jupiter's orbit where asteroids would be found. These points would be at angles of 60° from a line joining the sun and Jupiter itself, that is, ⅙ of the orbit ahead of Jupiter and ⅙ behind. More than a century later, in the early nineteen hundreds, asteroids were found in these locations. In 1959, the number had risen to 14, and there may be many more undiscovered, since asteroids are extremely difficult to observe at the distance of Jupiter. The asteroids east of Jupiter are usually named after Greek heroes of the Iliad—Ulysses, Nestor, Agamemnon; and those west of Jupiter are named after Trojan heroes—Priam, Aeneas, Troilus. However, before this procedure was started, Hector, a Trojan, was placed in the Greek camp—a spy had infiltrated. But all was well, since Patroclus, a Greek, had been misplaced in the Trojan camp—an interloper for the other side.

◀ Planet orbits are shown by broken lines; asteroid orbits by solid lines. Most of the asteroid orbits lie between Mars and Jupiter. Icarus moves closest to the sun; Hidalgo farthest from it. Most of the asteroids appear to move in the belts indicated. The Trojan asteroids move in Jupiter's orbit, preceding the planet and following it by about 60°.

When observed casually, the Trojans appear to move in a 12-year period, just as Jupiter does. However, careful study indicates that they move in a most complex fashion in and among themselves while sharing generally in preceding Jupiter by ⅙ of an orbit or following by the same amount.

Asteroids may number in the hundreds of thousands, and occasionally, as a meteorite, one may collide with the earth. Meteorites contain within them clues that may provide us with pieces to fit together the jigsaw puzzle of the origin and evolution of the asteroids and of the rest of the solar system. Tektites, which we discuss in the next chapter, may also provide some of the pieces of that puzzle.

Tektites | 3

At various places on the earth—Australia, Indochina, Africa, Czechoslovakia, and in Texas and Georgia in the United States—some 650,000 pieces of glasslike rock have been found. Most of them are very small, a millimeter or so across, and weigh only a few grams. They are called tektites, after the Greek word *tektos,* which means "molten." Tektites often look like glass that has been melted and then cooled into solid shapes: dumbbells, disks, rods, drops, spheres. Rarely one finds large tektites; the largest of all is about 32,000 grams and comes from Indochina. About 100 tektites found in the Philippines weigh between 200 and 700 grams. Some 500,000 tektites are believed to have been found in the Philippine Islands, the richest of all sources.

In this chapter we will be concerned with defining tektites, finding where they are most abundant, and suggesting sources where they may have originated.

Tektites look very much like black glass. When they were first found, people suggested that tektites were the remains of glass manufacturing that occurred in prehistoric times. Another theory was that tektites were formed when lightning struck sand, causing it to melt and fuse into globules of glass. About a hundred years ago the most popular theory held that tektites were like meteorites; they came out of the sky.

In the 1930's L. J. Spencer of the British Museum suggested that tektites came from the earth. He said that when a large meteorite or a comet nucleus struck the earth, soil and rock were melted by the heat of the impact. The temperature rose so fast that a tremendous explosion took place. The molten rock was thrown into the atmosphere, outward over long distances from the crater.

That may be and we'll take a closer look at the theory in just a moment. Other investigators believe that tektites came from the moon, not the earth. They say that asteroids, comets, or meteorites struck the moon and that the tektites are droplets of melted moon rocks that splashed from the moon and traveled to the earth. We'll explore this idea further, but first let's suppose tektites are made of earth-bound materials. What was their history? Quartz that has been melted and cooled has been found in tektites, and quartz melts at 1,710° Celsius. Other facts also point to a high temperature of formation. For example, there is very little water in tektites. High temperatures in the range believed necessary to form tektites can be reached naturally on the earth only by impacts such as those of meteorites. Furthermore, tektites appear to be the same size as they were when created. They do not appear to be pieces broken from larger formations, and they seem to have been molten for a very short time—only a few minutes at most. Impact of a meteorite could cause melting, the molten material could be thrown away from the earth, and the molten droplets cooled during their rapid transit through the atmosphere.

This theory is quite satisfactory for explaining the formation of tektites shaped like rods, spheres, teardrops, or dumbbells. But disks flattened in the center, called button tektites, have been found in Australia, and they pose problems. Some investigators say that the buttons were coin-shaped originally. As the disks passed downward through the atmosphere, the leading side melted. As material melted, it ablated (vaporized) much in the same manner that the leading face of a manned space capsule ablates. As the object slowed, the melted material would have flowed to the edge, making the familiar flanges found on the Australia buttons.

Other investigators believe these tektites were thrown out

Tektites occur in many sizes and shapes—rods, spheres, buttons, drops, dumbbells.

from the moon and acquired the flanged button shape during their one-way passage through earth's atmosphere. Perhaps they were, but let's look at the distribution of tektites before we go any further with our discussion.

Tektites are found in only a few locations, and they usually take the name of the region where they are found. For example, tektites from Czechoslovakia are called moldavites, those found in Australia are, naturally, called australites. The locations of tektite fields are shown on the map opposite.

True Tektites

NAME	NUMBER (APPROXIMATE)	SITE
Australites	40,000	Australia
Bediasites	2,000	Texas
Billitonites	7,500	Isle of Billiton (Java Sea)
Indochinites	40,000	Thailand
Ivory Coast tektites	200	Africa
Javaites	7,000	Borneo
Moldavites	55,000	Moldau River, Czechoslovakia
Philippinites	500,000	Philippine Islands

When the ages of a family of tektites are determined and their structure is studied, one finds that all the tektites in a family appear to have come from the same shower or occurrence. The oldest tektites turn out to be about 45 million years old, and the youngest only a few thousand years.

If tektites formed when meteorites or other objects crashed into the earth, there should be craters, or the remains of craters, made by the collisions. Tektites are so young there has not been sufficient time for the craters to have been smoothed out by erosion. In many cases the craters, or signs of them, have been located. However, searchers are at a loss to find a crater related to the australites. Crater remains have been located in Australia, but the crater was probably produced 250 million years ago. The australites are only about 5,000 years old, so they could not have been formed when that crater was produced. No recent crater has been located.

Some have suggested that the meteorite may have landed in the sea. But if it did, a tremendous tidal wave high enough to wash over the entire continent of Australia would have resulted.

Geologists find no signs of such a cataclysm. Some of them

The location of tektite finds in fields. The open circles are sites of meteorite impacts that may have produced the fields. The dot in the Atlantic represents a single tektite found on Martha's Vineyard.

believe that the fall may have occurred in Antarctica, and that a gigantic crater lies beneath the ice that covers the continent. So far none has been found.

Believers in the impact theory of tektite production argue that the meteorite (or comet nucleus) crashed into earth, melting rock which splashed out into the atmosphere. The rock cooled rapidly and the tektites, and other rubble, fell to the earth some hundreds, or thousands, of miles away. Others argue that tektites may have been formed by impact, but they were thrown into earth-circling orbits. The tektites entered the atmosphere at an angle low enough to cause a rather long passage through the atmosphere—long enough to produce the ablating that has been observed in the australite buttons.

Many investigators contend that tektites did not originate by impact. Perhaps lightning produced them, or great forest fires. Maybe they were blown out by volcanoes. Or, tektites may be pieces of the moon that have been ejected into space from lunar volcanoes, or by collisions of meteorites with the moon.

Lightning does fuse sand and soil occasionally. But tubes and rods are the products; not shapes that we find in tektites. Volcanic glasses and tektites do not match chemically, and also there are no volcanoes in the areas where tektites are found.

Scientists know that the magnetic field of the earth has been reversed many times during the geologic history of the earth. In their studies of the oceans, oceanographers have found microtektites in silts dated to the time of the last magnetic reversal. They argue that the laying down of the tektites and the magnetic reversals were due to a common cause. And they contend that the cause was a cosmic body of great size—perhaps the nucleus of a comet. It is reasonable to suppose that such a body may arrive every few hundred thousand years.

If such tremendous events do occur, the microtektites are

Fields of tektites may have been produced when meteorites struck the earth. Fused materials were thrown up in fountains that fell upon the surrounding areas. Powerful impacts may have fused material and accelerated some of it fast enough to go into earth-circling orbits—the tektites then falling into the sea or at isolated locations on land.

probably produced in the earth's atmosphere before impact. This may have been the case with the Tunguska event in Siberia in 1908. Microscopic bits of glassy material in abundance have been found in the area.

The search for the source of tektites remains one of the exciting quests of scientists. There are many who believe tektites are moon fragments that were blasted out of our neighbor world by cosmic collisions. They contend that the moon is bombarded constantly by meteorites, since there is no protecting atmosphere. The velocity of the meteorites is more than enough to throw debris into space, and the particles would escape the moon's gravitational field, and be moving fast enough to go into a sun-circling orbit. Over a period of a hundred million years the earth would sweep up a large amount of lunar debris.

The lunar material would go into orbit around the earth. As the orbit decays, stresses on large masses would cause the masses to break into smaller pieces. As the material moves through earth's atmosphere, the outer parts would be heated to high temperatures by friction. Melting would occur and droplets of material separate. The debris, moving in a long path through the atmosphere, would be exposed to heating and melting for a long time, often producing specialized shapes, such as the australite buttons mentioned earlier. This theory would explain why tektites are found in families that are strewn over a rather extensive area of the earth.

Theories of the origin of tektites generally settle upon bombardment as the fundamental cause. The main question seems to be whether the bombardment occurred on the surface of the earth or upon the surface of the moon. It was hoped that, when lunar rocks were studied, evidence would be found that would answer the question. So far, lunar samples, with one exception, have not supported the theory that tektites originated on the moon. The chemical composition of lunar rocks does not coin-

Tektites may originate on the moon. Large meteorites strike the moon, throwing out huge chunks of it which are captured by earth. The chunks break up as they enter earth's atmosphere. The pieces are strewn along the surface as shown. On subsequent passes any remaining particles would land west of the original fall.

cide with the makeup of tektites. At the same time, however, some of the microtektites, those found in ocean sediments, have compositions that are quite similar to those of the glasses found on the lunar surface.

The exception mentioned above is one rock in the Apollo 12 sample, material from Oceanus Procellarum (Ocean of Storms). This rock proved to have a composition quite different from the usual run of basaltic lunar rocks. Also, the per-

centage composition of this particular rock—number 12013—
was very much like that of one of the Java tektites, as shown
below:

SUBSTANCE	MOON ROCK NUMBER 12013	JAVA TEKTITE
Silicon dioxide	61%	63.5%
Titanium oxide	1.2	0.8
Aluminum oxide	12	12.6
Iron oxide	10	8.5
Magnesium oxide	6.0	6.8
Calcium oxide	6.3	3.8
Sodium oxide	0.69	0.7
Potassium oxide	2.0	1.5

The similarities between the two samples are impressive.
Judging by composition alone, they are quite alike, so much so
that one cannot say that the two did not have the same origin.
In addition to these similarities in composition, both tektites
and lunar rocks are very low in water content.

We are still looking for adequate explanations of the occurrence of tektites in limited areas. Although there are theories
concerning their origin, we still do not know how or where
tektites came into existence. Such questions challenge astrono-
mer-geologists. We have much knowledge about tektites and
many observations. Now the observations must be understood
and explained. And so it is with other mavericks of the solar
system—such as the organic molecules that have been identified.

Organic Molecules in
Meteorites and in Space

On May 14, 1864, a meteorite fell at the town of Orgueil, near Toulouse, in France. The major part of it (8.5 kilograms) is deposited in Paris, and a small part at the American Museum of Natural History in New York City. In 1961, less than a gram of the meteorite was studied by a group of scientists. They discovered complex hydrocarbon molecules in the sample. The molecules were very much like those formed here on the earth by living things. They were so similar that some scientists believed they had found fossil life in the Orgueil meteorite.

This was startling, if true. Could it be that life had originated in deep interplanetary space? Perhaps in the asteroid belt—assuming that belt to be the birthplace of meteorites (at least some of them)? Could it be that earthmen were not alone in the solar system, that there were other forms of life out among the planets, comets, and asteroids?

The meteorite that was studied was a stony meteorite, one called a carbonaceous chondrite. They are called chondrites because they contain chondrules—small, round objects. The chondrules are imbedded in a sooty, black material that contains considerable carbon.

Meteorites of this sort are very rare. Only about 20 of 700 meteorites seen to fall have turned out to be carbonaceous chondrites. There are other reasons for their rarity: They do not look like meteorites, and so only skilled investigators can identify them. Also, wind and rain destroy the meteorite rapidly. The only ones we know about were seen to fall and were collected soon after the event took place.

Organic molecules were found in the Orgueil meteorite. And they were found in other carbonaceous chondrites. But did the organic molecules have a biologic origin; did they come from living cells? That was the question.

Originally it was believed that all molecules that contained carbon were organic, and that they arose only in living organisms. But in the early part of the nineteenth century, organic molecules were produced in a laboratory, and nothing biological was involved. More recently, in 1953, Stanley Miller passed a discharge of electricity through a mixture of gases—ammonia, methane, water vapor, and hydrogen—and a series of complex organic molecules were produced. Several of the molecules were amino acids.

Opponents of the life-in-meteorites idea contended that meteorites were formed from primordial dust and gases. The gases could have been the same that Miller used in his research. In interplanetary space the gases would have been exposed to X-radiation, ultraviolet light, and cosmic rays; and it is reasonable to suppose that amino acids and other organic molecules could have been produced there just as they were created in Miller's laboratory.

When the announcement connecting meteorites with fossil life was made, other scientists looked carefully at other carbonaceous chondrites. Some of them thought they could identify fossil algae. If so, that would be sensational news.

But scientists for the most part did not accept the explana-

Steam (lower left) was combined with methane, ammonia, and hydrogen. When the mixture was exposed to an electrical discharge and then condensed, amino acids were produced.

tion a few investigators were making for their observations. Those who opposed the conclusion about fossil life said there are other possibilities. Maybe the molecules do represent fossil life, they said. But they might be crystals of organic compounds, such as those made by Miller; or they could be molecules that somehow got into the meteorites after they arrived on the earth or during their passage through the atmosphere. They might represent earth-based impurities.

How does a scientist know whether he's looking at a molecule produced by a living thing or one produced by a nonbiological process? It is not easy. However, it is believed that an essential ingredient in every biological cell is DNA (deoxyribonucleic acid). Careful study of several carbonaceous chondrites, including the Orgueil meteorite, indicates that DNA is not present. But this discovery is not final proof, for it is possible that DNA is not essential to living cells in the beginning of life itself. And the molecules in meteorites may be related to primitive life—life in the very early stages of evolution.

Small bits of a meteorite were ground up and put in a sterile culture. If there were any signs of life at all in the material, it might grow in the culture. After several months signs of growth could be seen in the culture medium. This may have meant that organisms that could grow were contained in the meteorite.

Dr. Brian Mason, who was a curator at the American Museum of Natural History when the "Orgueil" story was news, and who is now with the Smithsonian Institution, cautioned that it is extremely difficult to get a meteorite that has not been contaminated with earth-based materials. He says that many carbonaceous meteorites are porous. They are so porous that as they pass through earth's atmosphere they must take in molecules. After falling, the meteorites lie on the ground for periods of time during which they pick up molecules from the surface. Once they are found, the meteorites are handled by many people before they find their way to the cabinet of a museum, or a laboratory. Even there, they are open to the air. Dr. Mason feels that, when you consider the history of meteorites, it would be most remarkable to find one that did not contain spores, pollen grains, bacteria, or some other contaminant that originated on the earth. He believes that the growth in a culture medium was simply growth of the earth-based, or terrestrial, contaminant that the meteorite may have picked up as described above.

If an astronaut on the surface of the moon could catch a meteorite before it struck the lunar surface, we would have a specimen unchanged by any terrestrial or lunar environment. The meteorite and the molecules in it would be as they were in space itself. It would be fascinating to study such a specimen in the germ-free, high vacuum laboratory of the moon. Such a meteorite may be caught sometime, or possibly an astronaut will be able to capture one from a space station in orbit around the earth. When that happens we'll be able to establish for certain whether or not the molecules that have been observed in these fascinating meteorites are produced in space or if they are introduced after the object enters earth's environment.

There are some investigators who want to believe the organic molecules in meteorites are a sign of fossil life. At the same time, there are others who do not support such a belief. But regardless of what they mean, we do know that in parts of outer space, and at times long past, complex molecules came into being. The carbonaceous chondrites may be remnants of the basic material from which the sun and planets were formed. Or, as some investigators contend, these carbonaceous sooty meteorites may have been formed from other stony meteorites when chemicals—water, hydrogen, and carbon—were introduced. They may have their origin in one or more specific regions of the asteroid belt.

Another aspect of the carbonaceous chondrites is especially fascinating to you and me, for these humble objects may be the springboard of our own existence. It's not unreasonable to suppose that the earth formed when meteoritic material packed together in ages long ago. If some of this meteoritic material carried complex organic substances, amino acids, it would be much easier for the biologist to understand how cells that could grow and replace themselves would evolve. As Dr. Mason says, "Perhaps the organic compounds of the carbonaceous chondrites hold the key to the origin of life on this planet."

Beyond the solar system, in the vast desolate and seemingly endless reaches of interstellar space, radio astronomers have found complex molecules: simple amino acids, carbon monoxide, formaldehyde, ammonia, methyl alcohol, water, and many more. One wonders if these molecules are in any way connected with the molecules we find in meteorites that exist in our own "local" area.

Just as the organic molecules of meteorites may be precursors of life, so also may the molecules that radio astronomers are identifying.

The ammonia molecules were discovered by radio astronomy techniques. They were found at many locations, but rather abundantly in large, cool gas and dust clouds in the direction of Sagittarius, toward the center of the Milky Way Galaxy.

These complex molecules are rare, and they are short-lived. Interstellar ammonia, for example, amounts to only about one molecule per liter. For comparison, most of the material in the dust cloud is hydrogen, and astronomers believe the concentration of hydrogen molecules in the cloud is in the order of a million molecules per liter.

Conditions in interstellar space are much too severe for molecules to survive. For example, the ultraviolet light is so intense that ammonia molecules would be broken into the nitrogen and hydrogen atoms of which they are made. But when the molecules are distributed inside the cloud of dust and other gases they are protected to some degree, and so endure for a longer time.

In the 1930's it was commonly believed that space be-

Radio telescopes have enabled astronomers to identify many ▶
materials, including molecules, that exist in outer space.

tween the stars was empty. However, careful observation reveals that there is no such thing as empty space. Interstellar
space contains gases and simple and complex molecules usually
referred to collectively as cosmic dust. And these gases and dust
particles between the stars may be the building material out of
which stars are created. Planets may be formed out of the same
material as it condenses, and some of the gases may become
planetary atmosphere.

Ammonia and methane are present in the atmospheres of
both Jupiter and Saturn, and probably also of Uranus and Neptune. Very likely at one time in the early history of our own
planet, ammonia and methane were part of our atmosphere.
Perhaps these substances played a major part in forming the
first organic molecules. Miller showed how this might have
occurred.

Maybe there is no connection between phenomena observed in interplanetary space and those that exist in interstellar space. But scientists continue to explore possibilities. They
are concerned with the study of comets. Some few move in
orbits reaching halfway to the distant stars, and some come
within a few million miles of the earth. Indeed, comets may
have collided with earth at some time in its evolution.

Comets | 5

Certain famous astronomers are associated with objects or discoveries: Galileo with the telescope, Copernicus with the solar system, and most certainly the name of Halley is connected with comets.

Many people have discovered more comets than did Edmund Halley; many have studied the composition of comets more extensively. But Edmund Halley (1656–1742) discovered that comets move in orbits around the sun, that they often make return visits, and that they do not arise spontaneously out of nothing.

After observing the comet of 1680, Sir Isaac Newton figured out that the comet must move in a very flat elliptical orbit. Edmund Halley, a friend and collaborator of Newton's, became deeply interested in comets. He studied the records of comets and found there were similarities between comets that had appeared in 1531 and 1607, and when the comet of 1682 appeared, he found that all three appeared to be related.

After careful figuring, Halley maintained that these were not different comets but were three appearances of the same comet. Furthermore, he predicted that the comet would reappear 75 years later. Other mathematicians of the day checked the figures of Halley. They agreed, but said that Jupiter and Saturn would delay the comet by about 618 days. After their work was done, they said the comet would pass perihelion in April 1759. (Perihelion is the location in an orbit nearest the sun, from *peri*, "near," and *helios*, "sun.")

One month early, March 12, 1759, the comet reappeared.

The orbit of Halley's comet is tilted 17° to the plane of the solar system. The comet rises above the plane just inside the orbit of Mars. Its 75-year period takes it out beyond the orbit of Neptune.

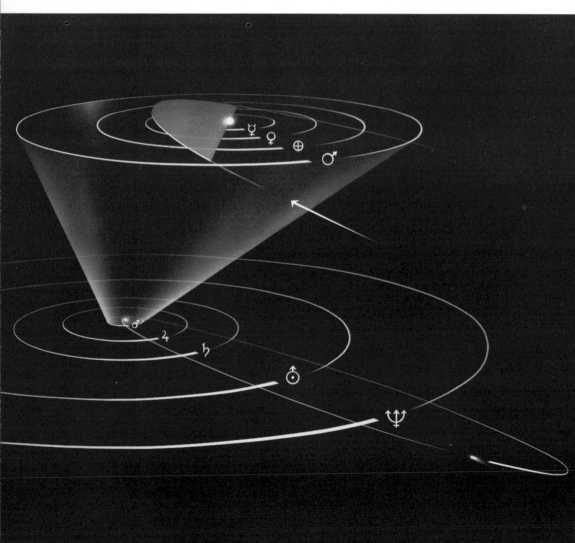

Unfortunately, Halley did not live to see the reappearance of the comet that was named after him. The comet's recurrence established that comets were part of the solar system. Much of their mystery was removed, and a new era of comet investigation began.

Every 75 years, or thereabouts (the time varies somewhat because of the effect of the gravitation of the planets), Halley's comet reappears. In 1909–1910, its last appearance, it was first sighted on September 11, 1909. For several months astronomers watched the comet. In March and April, 1910, the comet swung close to the sun and became invisible. About April 18 it became visible again. It grew brighter, reaching its greatest brightness (magnitude 2) on May 10. (A magnitude 2 brightness is equal to the brightness of a fairly bright star.) The tail grew steadily, reaching a length of some 140° on May 20. (Remember that it is 180° from one horizon to the other.) This is when the earth passed through the tail. In spite of the warnings of alarmists, no evil effects were experienced.

Before and since the time of Edmund Halley, comets have fascinated astronomers and laymen alike. Some 2,000 have been discovered, many no doubt reappearances of comets that have been seen before. Frequent sightings are listed below.

Periodic Comets Observed Ten or More Times

COMET	PERIOD (YEARS)	CLOSEST APPROACH (AU)	OBSERVATIONS
Encke	3.30	0.338	45
Tempel II	5.30	1.391	12
Pons-Winnecke	6.12	1.159	15
D'Arrest	6.70	1.378	10
Faye	7.41	1.652	14
Halley	76.03	0.587	29

What a thrill it must be to make a real discovery, to see a galaxy never seen before, to identify craters on Mars, to find a satellite of a planet, or to discover a new comet—one that has never been observed by any man. The thrills of most discoveries are usually reserved for the professional astronomer. But this is not the case with comets. In fact, the larger number of comets have been discovered by amateurs, although that is changing now. Some comets have been found by amateurs using telescopes they have made themselves. That's how it was with Kaoru Ikeya, who lives in the small village of Bentenjima, Japan. At latest count, five comets are named after him, either alone or jointly with a codiscoverer.

Ikeya discovered his first comet on January 2, 1963, when he was nineteen years old. He used an 8-inch telescope that he had built himself. Each morning, before he went to work to help support his fatherless family, Ikeya donned warm clothes and went to the flat roof of his house. He uncovered his telescope and scanned the sky, hoping to find a wispy light spot in the dark sky, a spot that changed position from night to night.

After months of cold, tedious observing, Ikeya sighted a small faint cloud that he had never seen before. He consulted his star maps to see if any object was charted there, but found nothing. Ikeya went back to the eyepiece. The object was still there. He wasn't positive but he thought he was looking at a new comet. As soon as the telegraph office was open Ikeya sent a wire to the Tokyo Astronomical Observatory, giving the position of the object he had seen and identifying himself as the discoverer.

The news was sent around the world. Professional astronomers turned their telescopes to the location given by Ikeya and, sure enough, they saw the comet. It was called Comet Ikeya 1963a. The *a* indicated it was the first comet discovered in 1963.

Since that day in January Ikeya has built a larger telescope, and he has discovered four other comets. One of these was also discovered on the same night by Tsutomu Seki, an amateur astronomer who lived about 240 miles from Ikeya. It was called Ikeya-Seki 1967n (the 14th comet discovered in 1967). Comets are often discovered simultaneously by different observers. They may carry as many as three names, in honor of the people who discover them.

After the discovery-year has passed, comets are numbered in the order that they pass through perihelion. For example, Ikeya-Seki 1967n is now called Ikeya-Seki VII, the seventh comet to go through perihelion. When professionals are at their telescopes, they have certain jobs to do—particular stars to photograph or certain galaxies to study. Also, until fairly recently, they used telescopes that picked up a very small part of the total sky. With such instruments, astronomers did not have time to scan the sky, a procedure essential to comet-finding. However, telescopes that cover and photograph a wide field are changing that because pictures are scanned carefully and faint objects, such as comets, show up clearly.

A professional comet hunter is Dr. Lubos Kohoutek, a Czech, who, on March 7, 1973, discovered what was expected to become the most spectacular comet of the century. Kohoutek used a large telescope at the Hamburg Observatory in West Germany. The comet, after passing through perihelion on December 28 of that year, did not become brighter, as expected. Perhaps a crust of some sort had formed around the nucleus, preventing gases from escaping.

Each year, six or eight new comets are found, on the average. As more amateurs get better telescopes and as more observatories make wide-field photographs of the sky, we expect the number of discoveries to increase. About 2,000 comets have been observed and studied, but there are probably millions of them in the solar system; some astronomers say there

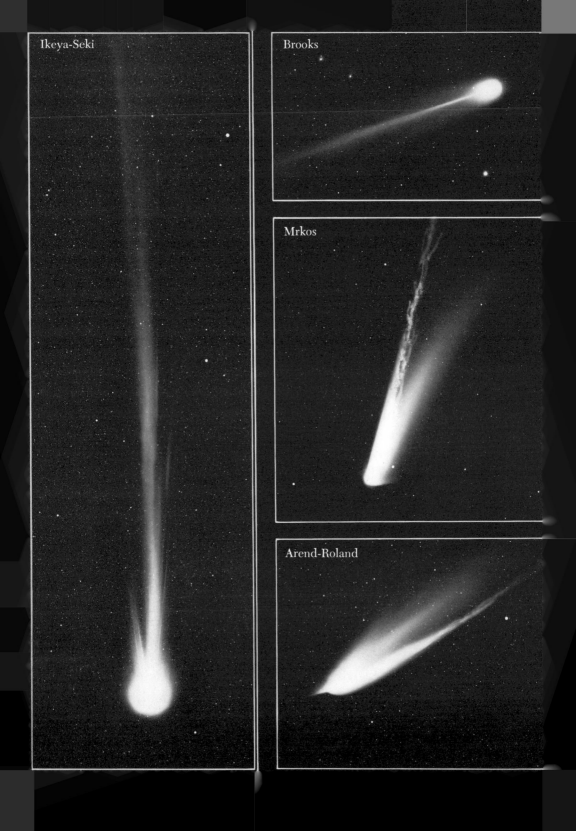

are 100 billion. Most of the comets are very dim. When at great distances from the sun they are not easily identified, for they look like fuzzy stars. The streaming comet tails do not develop until a comet gets close to the sun. By far the larger number of comets never get close enough for a tail to form.

A few astronomers who have studied comets thought of them as flying gravel banks, great masses of tiny solid particles held together by their own gravitational attraction. This theory of the makeup of a comet has several weaknesses and it has been largely abandoned. For example, we know that a comet tail is made up of gases, and solid particles could not produce the amount of gas observed.

Around 1950, another and more popular idea about comets was presented. It's possible that comets may be found billions of miles from the sun. Maybe they exist in the space halfway to Alpha Centauri, the nearest star beyond the sun. Or, at least, they may arise out of materials in the interstellar space that extends that far. If so, we know that hydrogen is the most abundant material, and helium is the second most common substance. The next most prevalent materials are carbon, nitrogen, and oxygen. Therefore, comets should contain these substances and combinations of them, such as methane (CH_4), ammonia (NH_3), and water(H_2O). But such molecules have not yet been identified.

A comet may be a big snowball containing simple compounds, such as CH, NH, CN compounds. Imbedded in this snow and ice would be sodium, iron, nickel, chromium, dust, substances that remain solid and do not vaporize easily. After careful study of the tails of comets, an astronomer concluded that a minimum of 150 million tons of iron in the tail would explain the sunlight reflected by the tail. This seems like a tremendous amount of iron. Actually, it is very little, considering the volume of the tail. When a comet is near the sun, the tail develops rapidly. The rate of formation of the tail requires that

The tail becomes longer as a comet approaches the sun. It always points from the sun, pushed away by the solar wind. Here earth (inner orbit) passes through the comet tail.

the comet lose at least 100 tons of iron each second while close to the sun. Comets such as those studied can make about 100 close approaches to the sun before they lose the ability to develop comet tails. This means that the comet must contain some 10 billion tons of iron. This sounds like a tremendous amount, and it is. But if iron makes up $\frac{1}{20}$ of the total comet, which is reasonable, the comet would contain only one billionth the material contained in the earth.

Most of the millions (or perhaps billions) of comets which belong to the solar system move in orbits always distant from the sun, so far away that they remain forever cold cosmic snowballs.

The orbits of certain comets might be disrupted by a close

approach to Jupiter, Saturn, or another of the major planets. If we assume the gravitational force of Jupiter is 1,000, the relative effects of other planets and the sun are shown below, assuming the same distance between each planet (or the sun) and the comet.

Sun	1,047,350	Earth	3.2
Jupiter	1,000	Venus	2.6
Saturn	299	Mars	0.34
Neptune	54	Mercury	0.17
Uranus	46		

To an observer on earth the tail of the comet at the left appears longer than that of the comet on the right. (Note the lengths of the double-headed arrows.) Apparent length depends upon the location of the comet and the viewer.

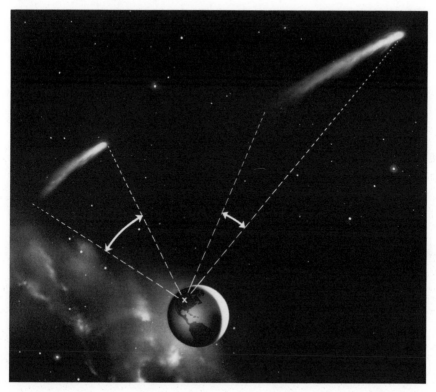

The attraction by a planet changes the orbit enough to bring the comet closer to the sun. The snowball theory holds that, as a comet gets near the sun, heat causes the frozen material to change to gases. Solids held in the snowball are set free and produce a stream of material that eventually results in spectacular meteor displays. Radiation from the sun, especially the ultraviolet radiation, breaks down complex molecules (ammonia, CH_4; methane, NH_3) into much simpler fragments—C_2, OH, CN, NH. The simpler compounds have been identified in comets, while the more complex ones of methane, ammonia, and water have not.

The snowball model of a comet makes it possible to explain the jets of gases that are sometimes ejected from comets, as shown below. Porous layers of solids, a sort of crust, may surround the icy material in the core of a comet. As the comet nears the sun, radiation breaks through the crust here

Explosive expansion and ejection of gases from the nuclei of comets may be the cause of the jets that are occasionally observed.

and there, vaporizes the ices, and the gases once set free shoot out in long, tenuous jets.

When a comet's orbit is changed so much that it strays into the inner part of the solar system, one would expect the comet would not last very long. However, they often survive for thousands of years. The crust mentioned above may be part of the reason. It would prevent rapid evaporation, serving to slow down the separation of the comet into the gases and solids of which it is composed.

This snowball theory refers only to the nucleus of a comet. There are three principal parts, though all of them cannot be observed readily: the tail of the comet, the nucleus (the frozen materials and dust mentioned above), and the coma (hazy, glowing materials that surround the nucleus).

The nucleus of a small comet may be only a mile or two in diameter, but the coma may extend for thousands of miles beyond—80,000 to 100,000 miles would not be impossible. Halley's comet, the one that we hear about frequently, is believed to have a nucleus not more than 20 miles in diameter, but its coma is thousands of miles across; and, during its last approach in the fall of 1909 and the spring of 1910, its tail extended 150 million miles across the sky.

WHERE COMETS COME FROM

A good many comets were discovered long before the telescope was invented. Observers scanned large areas of the sky with their unaided eyes. Even though they could not discern objects beyond the range of human seeing ability (about 6th magnitude), these early observers were able to make many discoveries because they were patient, they could see large segments of the sky, and they had good seeing conditions.

The telescope made it possible to see much dimmer objects, and as telescopes improved, the range of seeing was extended. Each year larger numbers of comets are discovered. All of them, even the very dim and therefore most distant comets, belong to our solar system. They move in elliptical orbits with the sun at one of the foci of the ellipse.

Careful study of the orbits of comets indicates that at one time many were in the region between 50,000 and 200,000 astronomical units (AU) from the sun. (Alpha Centauri, the nearest star, is about 300,000 AU from the sun.) These far-off comets move in almost circular orbits around the sun. Unless affected by some force outside themselves, these cosmic snowballs would remain in the same orbits forever.

About half of those that were originally closer, some 10,000 AU from us, have left the region and have been picked up by other stars. Assuming that all comets, or at least the materials of which they are made, came into existence when the solar system was formed, the distant comets have been under the influence of the sun some 5 billion years, a rough figure for the age of the solar system. Nearly all of those comets beyond 100,000 AU have been pulled away by distant stars.

However, many astronomers believe that a great cloudlike layer of comets still exists some 150,000 AU from the sun. Most of them move in nearly circular orbits, and so we shall never see them. Occasionally, the orbit of one of these comets will be altered by the attraction of the sun or Jupiter. The orbit will become slightly elliptical. After perhaps millions of years, the orbit will be modified to such an extent that the comet moves close enough to earth for it to be observed. Astronomers believe that only 1 in 100,000 ever goes through this history. Chances are there are some 100 billion comets in the cloud layer. But there is very little material in all the comets put together; probably not more than 1/10 of that contained in our own planet.

Analysis of the light of comets reveals the presence of many different substances—carbon, nitrogen, oxygen, nickel, iron—all of which had to have some origin. It is generally accepted that the sun and the planets had a common beginning. Perhaps there was a gigantic nebula, a cloud of gases, that gradually formed into a flattened disk. As ages went by, certain of the atoms would have concentrated together. The resulting mass would have attracted additional molecules. As the mass increased, its attraction would increase. Such concentrations would have formed throughout the primordial nebula. In time, the greater of these masses would have become stars, and the lesser may have become planets.

Leftover material in this vast solar nebula may have become the comets, making the cloud that extends halfway to Alpha Centauri.

Comets in this outer swarm take a million years or more to go around the sun. Every few million years, stars pass within a few light-years of the sun. They would change the orbit of a comet, making it more elliptical, and it might make a closer approach to the sun. After a few million years the comet might be deflected still more, and it might be pulled into the inner solar system. There it might move in an elliptical orbit having its perihelion in the vicinity of Jupiter, let us say, an orbit that may be completed in only a few years. Halley's comet, for example, has a period of 76 years, and Encke's comet completes an orbit in only 3 years—the shortest period of all.

The lifetimes of such comets cannot exceed more than a few million years at the most, and perhaps they are much shorter. Every time they go around the sun, material from the nucleus is vaporized to produce the comet's tail. And most of that material never returns to the nucleus. It is ejected into space—spewed along the comet's orbit. The nucleus, which may have been only a few miles across at the start, is reduced in size and mass. Eventually the material will dissipate completely, and the comet will no longer exist.

COMET LORE

Scientists now have a pretty good idea of the makeup of comets, their origin, and their history; and they understand why comets move in the orbits that are observed. Nevertheless, much of the folklore and legends of comets that originated in the Middle Ages, and even long before, persist to the present day in some parts of the world.

From the very earliest times, comets were associated with famine and disease, epidemic, hunger, pestilence and death. The appearance of a comet was supposed to signal the death of a prince or ruler. The comet was frequently thought to be the finger of a god pointing toward the earth, warning the people of an evil to be visited upon them. Comets were called disasters; indeed the word means "evil" (*dis*) "star" (*aster*).

People thought of comets as fiery swords or crosses dripping with blood, daggers imbedded in flames, foretelling calamity on the earth. In 1528 a comet was described as follows:

> This comet was so horrible and terrifying, and it aroused such fear among the populace, that some died of fright as a result, while others fell ill. It appeared to be exceedingly long and was of the colour of blood; at the top, the figure of a bent arm was visible, holding a great sword in its hand as though about to strike. At the point of the sword there were three stars. At the two sides of the rays of this comet, there were seen a great number of axes, knives, and blood-stained swords among which were many hideous human faces with their beards and hairs standing on end.

Today most people who observe comets are not so terrified. However, almost invariably when a comet is reported, fantastic stories of its effect on people are revived, or dire results of a collision between a comet and the earth are suggested. One hears predictions that the moon will go into an orbit that will result in its loss to the earth, or the earth will move into a new orbit that will take it far from the sun, causing its temperature to drop below the level necessary to support life. In addition one hears that the earth will be tilted to such an extent that both the northern and southern hemispheres will experience six months of darkness followed by six months of daylight; or that rain will fall upon the entire earth for days, weeks, and months, flooding all land surfaces and destroying civilization.

Actually, collisions between a comet and the earth are extremely rare. In 1910 earth was surrounded by the tail of Halley's comet, but there was no effect of the event. It is true that cyanogen and carbon monoxide, two poisonous gases, are contained in a comet's tail. But the gases are so thin, only a molecule or so in a cubic meter of space, that one would not be affected at all by them. And, actually, the gases never reach earth's surface. They are trapped and further diluted by earth's outer atmosphere, which is extremely rare by comparison with air at earth's surface, but extremely dense when compared with the density of a comet.

Particles in the nucleus of a comet are packed together much more closely. Therefore, should a cometary nucleus collide with the earth, considerable effects would be felt. If the particles in the nucleus were sparse, there would be a spectacular display of meteors, fireballs (tremendous bursts of light), and bolides (light bursts accompanied by snaps and crackles). If the nucleus were tightly packed together, and so only a mile or so across, it could cause widespread destruction. You recall it is believed that the Tunguska was a small comet nucleus that entered the atmosphere above Siberia in 1908. The particles were heated white hot. The hot mass crashed into the earth with tremendous energy, spreading destruction over an area some 100 miles across.

So rare are collisions with comets that millions of years may pass before there is another one. So, if you see a comet don't be alarmed. It is a great cosmic snowball making a brief, bright visit to the inner part of the solar system, soon to journey into the cold, unbelievably distant isolation of deep interplanetary space where it will perhaps be lost forever to man's scrutiny.

Comets are dramatic happenings, unpredictable except for those that have definite periods. One sees them only occasionally. Other celestial events are more common. One of these is the zodiacal light which can be observed regularly, although it is not especially spectacular.

The Zodiacal Light | 6

In the tropics and occasionally at other locations, a hazy patch of light appears in the evening sky. It is the zodiacal light, produced, in part at least, by light reflecting from solid particles that abound in space.

The name of this soft glow comes from the zodiac, the region of the sky in which it appears. In the course of one year the sun seems to move from one constellation to another; from the Fishes to the Ram, to the Bull, and so on around the sky. This apparent motion of the sun results from earth's revolution around the sun. Actually we do not see both the sun and the constellations at the same time. However, we see the succession of constellations in the western sky at sunset, appearing daily as the year goes by and after the sun has disappeared. Year in and year out the sun makes the journey around the zodiac. The constellations through which the sun seems to move make up the zodiac, or the zodiacal belt. The word comes from the Greek word *zoon*, meaning "animal." It's the same word from which we get *zoology*, and *zoo*. All except one of the constellations (Libra, the scale) are named for animals—bull, ram, fishes, crab, to name a few. The glow of light appears in a particular part of the sky, the zodiac, so the name zodiacal light is given to the phenomenon.

The belt of the zodiac is vertical to the horizon, or nearly so, all through the year in the tropics. In latitudes north and south of the tropics the belt is often almost parallel to the horizon. The zodiacal light can best be seen in the tropics where the belt is vertical, and so extends well above the horizon where the glow of sunset may persist.

The light is no brighter than the dim parts of the Milky Way. For this reason, it can be seen only when the dimmer sections of the Milky Way are in the evening sky—in the springtime of the year. The zodiac cannot be seen within 18° of the sun. Therefore, the sun must be that many degrees below the horizon. Once visible, the zodiacal light can be seen for only about an hour.

However, one can often discern the zodiacal light in the morning sky, just preceding sunrise. The morning zodiacal light is dimmer than that of the evening. Nevertheless, the earliest historical references to the light are concerned with the morning and not the evening phenomenon. The references come from people who lived in the Near Eastern countries, many of whom had religious festivals that were timed from sunrise. Sometimes priests must have mistaken the zodiacal light for dawn (which occurs up to an hour later) and so the religious festivals were timed improperly. The zodiacal light of the morning was called "the false dawn" for this reason, and is still referred to in this manner in some parts of the world.

Careful and regular observations of the zodiacal light were first made in the seventeenth century. The Italian astronomer Jean Dominique Cassini, who later became a French citizen, is usually given credit for these observations. Actually it was not he who made them, but one of his assistants, a man by the name of Niccolo Fatio. He observed the light on many occasions. On the basis of Fatio's observations, Cassini suggested that the light might be produced by sunlight reflecting from masses of small particles in orbit around the sun, a suggestion that is well supported today. Advanced and sensitive equipment indicated that free electrons might contribute considerable light. However, most astronomers now believe that electrons are not that important, and most of the light is sunlight reflected from very small particles, only about a thousandth of an inch across.

Should you ever see the zodiacal light, it will appear as a

The zodiacal light appears along the ecliptic (broken line in the inset) after the sun has disappeared below the horizon.

cone of light, tapering to a tip. However, skilled observers on occasion have noticed that a faintly luminous band of light often extends beyond the tip of the western cone, apparently going all around the sky. This implies that the particles that produce the light must exist far beyond the earth. This band is extremely elusive, hard to identify, and for many years was never noticed. Before the belt was seen clearly, observers believed that the particles extended no farther than Venus.

When the sky is clear and dark and there is no moon, it is sometimes possible to see a faint glow directly opposite the sun's location, the *anti-solar point*. The German naturalist Alexander von Humboldt saw the light on several occasions in the early seventeen hundreds. He reported that he had seen the zodiacal light and the counterglow of the sun. Humboldt used the German word *Gegenschein* for counterglow and ever since that word has been used to refer to the phenomenon. Its nature is still in doubt but a disk of tiny particles around the sun and extending some million miles beyond the earth might reflect sunlight in such a way that a spot appears. Each of the particles on the opposite side of the earth from the sun would catch light and reflect it to an observer on earth, producing the *Gegenschein*. Particles at other locations would also be lighted by the sun, but not enough light to be noticeable would be scattered toward the earth.

The cloud of particles in the zodiacal band around the sun seems to be a lens-shaped doughnut, thickest toward the center and tapering off as distance from the sun increases. We do not know how far into space the cloud extends, but certainly it reaches well beyond the orbit of our own planet.

The cloud is not continuous from the sun on out. It could not be, for there is a zone around the sun where the temperature is so hot the particles would vaporize.

You may be wondering about the size of the particles that

One explanation of the zodiacal light. Broken line represents the observer's horizon. After sunset, sunlight striking particles in space is reflected to the observer. He sees this as a glow, as shown on page 79. The zodiacal light appears in the belt of the zodiac. Here in the fall the sun is in Leo.

comprise the dust cloud. Assuming they are in orbit around the sun, we can apply some facts to find the answer. Small grains, or flakes, are not heated evenly by the sun. The sun side gets hot, while the side away from the sun remains cool. This temperature difference shifts the center of balance of the particles and results in a very slight drop in velocity. The particle cannot hold its orbit, so it moves ever so slightly inward toward the sun. The process is repeated over and over, resulting in the particle following a spiral path rather than an elliptical path.

Large bodies, say half an inch across, would spiral into the sun in about 20 million years. Small particles microscopic in size are more strongly affected. They would reach the sun in only a million years or so. In certain cases, when the size of the particles is very small and their density is low, they are literally blown away from the sun by radiation pressure and escape from the solar system.

Therefore, in a few million years space should be swept clean of small particles. Only those half an inch or so across, or larger, should be left. But the zodiacal light results from small particles. Could they have been produced only a million years ago? If so, where did they come from?

People used to think that the dust clouds that make the zodiacal light were remnants of creation. Suppose the earth were formed 4.5 billion years ago. Certainly space would have been swept clear of remnants of such small size. We must look elsewhere for sources of the particles.

Comets are possibilities. Comets are as near to nothing as anything can be and still be something. That's true for the "tail" of a comet. But the head is believed to be made of particles imbedded in frozen gases. Whenever a comet moves close to the sun or to another massive body—Jupiter, for example—the comet head is pulled apart to some extent. Gases evaporate, and the solid particles continue in their orbit around the sun.

They become more spread apart as time goes by. Some of this diffuse dust may replenish the cloud of particles that produces the zodiacal light.

Another possible source of dust particles is the asteroids. There are untold numbers of asteroids in the space between the orbits of Mars and Jupiter. Some of them are very large— several hundred miles across; and some are very small.

Occasionally there must be collisions between asteroids, causing them to break up into small pieces and also producing very fine particles. The orbits of the particles would be changed, and some of them would drift in toward the sun, others would be blown away by the solar wind. After eons of time the particles drifting into the sun end up as gases, vaporized by the high temperature.

There are probably millions of comets in the solar system that could supply these particles, and the effects of the solar wind, a phenomenon that originates in the sun and extends to the earth and far beyond are always present.

The Solar Wind | 7

Every second the sun ejects a million tons of hydrogen. The hydrogen races into space at speeds up to a million miles per hour, producing an enlarging sphere with the sun at the center. It is called the solar wind. The wind sweeps up gases, fine particles of dust, and even cosmic particles. Scientists believe the solar wind is closely connected with aurora displays (the Northern Lights and Southern Lights), with storms in the earth's magnetic field, and with the structure and activity in the outer portion of the radiation belts that surround the earth. The solar wind may also have some effect on our day-to-day weather.

The presence of solar particles in outer space had been suspected for a long time before they were discovered. As early as 1672 the astronomer Cassini suggested that the zodiacal light was produced by a cloud of "dust" around the sun. Other scientists explained auroras by suggesting that solar particles caused them. Definite proof of the existence of the solar wind was not obtained until the early years of the Space Age when spacecraft actually measured the presence of particles and their activity. Further proof was obtained by the Apollo experiments which were placed upon the moon. A roll of aluminum foil was mounted atop a pole stuck into the lunar surface. About four feet of foil was unrolled and placed at right angles to the sun. After several hours, the foil was rolled up and the reel was brought back to earth. Scientists found that helium (He^3,He^4) and neon (Ne^{20},Ne^{22}) had been collected.

The main component of the solar wind, however, is hydrogen; not the gas, but hydrogen ions (protons). An ion is an electrified particle—in this case a proton carrying a positive charge. The effect of these protons upon the tails of comets is one of the most observable proofs of the solar wind.

When a comet moves in toward the sun a tail of gas usually develops, in some cases extending millions of miles from the head of the comet. The tail points away from the sun at all times—whether the comet is moving toward the sun or away, it does not matter. For several decades the pressure of sunlight was given as an explanation. This is not unreasonable, for light does exert pressure, but the amount of pressure, even in the case of sunlight, is not great. In fact, in the early 1950's we found that the pressure of sunlight was not nearly great enough to cause comet gas tails to behave as they do. Only high-speed particles streaming from the sun could cause such gas tails to develop and assume the observed shapes and patterns. Analysis of the light of comet tails indicates the existence of molecule fragments that are usually thought to be produced by collisions with high-speed particles (in this case, protons).

About this time observers learned that particles are radiated from the sun all the time. Previously, they had thought that the particles were ejected from the sun only when there were severe solar flares—sudden explosive bursts in small areas of the sun accompanied by increased light—or that the particles were ejected out of sunspot centers in some unexplained fashion. But the particles stream from the sun at all times.

Comet tails are pushed along by the particles. Dr. E. H. Parker, who has made many contributions to our knowledge of the solar wind and who introduced the name, has called comet tails interplanetary "wind socks." They "fly" with the solar wind just as a wind sock at an airport "flies" in the direction the wind is blowing. On certain occasions comet tails would be affected more strongly than at other times, indicating sudden bursts of intensity in the solar wind. The behavior of comet tails is proof enough that the solar wind blows continually throughout the solar system.

The solar wind originates somewhere in the sun, and it is continuous; therefore scientists had to look for some continuous activity in the sun that could produce the solar wind. The solar corona, the outer part of the solar atmosphere, was studied intensely. Careful analysis showed that the gases in the solar corona were very thin. There are only 100 million to a billion hydrogen atoms in each cubic centimeter of the corona. In the air we breathe there are 100 billion times as many.

The individual atoms in the corona move very fast, at a velocity that can be achieved only when the temperature is in the order of a million degrees. Atoms cannot exist at such a temperature; only fragments of atoms—ions and electrons. Because protons are so light and so abundant in the sun, they make up the bulk of the solar wind. As the protons escape so do electrons—the particles that produce the hydrogen atom when joined together.

The temperature of the photosphere of the sun (the part that we see) is about 6,000°C., and one would expect the part of the sun beyond the photosphere to be cooler. But it is much hotter. This poses a perplexing problem for astrophysicists, one which they attempt to answer as follows: The density of the corona is very low, therefore the ions composing it can move readily. Very little energy is needed to raise the temperature a considerable amount. The photosphere of the sun is very active, the gases constantly churning about. It has been suggested that waves of energy are generated by this action. The waves carry energy into the rarefied corona where the electrified particles pick it up. This constant wave motion builds upon itself as it moves outward.

During a solar eclipse, the solar corona can be seen extending sometimes 1 million miles beyond the solar surface. Many scientists feel that if we were able to view the corona without interfering haze and light, we might see it extending

The extent and shape of the solar corona vary with solar activity; here it is shown at a rather active time.

much farther into space, even to the earth and beyond. Indeed we have found that there is a temperature increase in the outer reaches of earth's atmosphere. The increase can be accounted for by assuming that the hot solar corona engulfs our planet, and there is a heat transfer from the corona to our atmosphere.

According to one line of reasoning (if we use the lower figure for the density of the solar wind), the solar wind terminates a little beyond Saturn. However, using the upper figure for density, it may continue way beyond Pluto, perhaps three or four times as far. If we use the astronomical unit as a measuring unit, we could say that the extent of the solar wind is somewhere between 12 AU (a bit beyond Saturn) and 160 AU (four times the distance to Pluto).

By the mid-1980's space probes will reach the regions of the outer planets, Uranus, Neptune, and Pluto. They will be equipped with counters that will measure the density and flow of the solar wind. These probes may transmit information back to the earth that will enable scientists to conclude that the solar wind terminates either somewhere within the area covered by the orbit of the probe, or somewhere beyond Pluto.

THE MAGNETOSPHERE AND RADIATION BELTS

It has been known for several decades that the upper atmosphere of the earth, called the ionosphere, is highly electrified with ions and electrons. In the last decade, space probes have revealed that the earth is also surrounded by belts of high-energy ionized particles. Collectively they are called the Van Allen belts, after the scientist who first explained their presence, or simply the radiation belts. When they were first discovered in 1958, by the early Explorer satellites, we thought the belts were shaped somewhat like doughnuts, earth being in the hole of the doughnut. Further study revealed that the belts are not symmetrical. They are flattened on the solar side and elongated on the side away from the sun, and they existed inside the earth's magnetosphere, the region where earth's magnetic field has influence.

The magnetopause, or boundary, of the magnetosphere is an interface where solar wind particles, which are ions, interact with earth's magnetic field. Most of the solar wind particles are deflected into space by earth's magnetic field. However, some of the particles penetrate the magnetopause and become trapped in the Van Allen belts. When the belts are overloaded, excess particles spill over and into the upper atmosphere, producing the aurora displays seen in the north and south arctic regions.

As the illustration shows, the magnetosphere is compressed on the sun side. This is due to the "pressure" of the solar wind particles. However, the magnetosphere streams for millions of miles away from the sun-earth system; it "flows" with the solar wind. Earth is surrounded by the solar wind, and the solar wind is affected strongly by the presence of the earth.

We would not expect other planets except Jupiter to affect the solar wind so markedly, because as far as we can determine Jupiter and the earth alone possess significant global magnetic fields.

Studies of the moon, Venus, and Mars by probes and land-based instruments have not revealed magnetic fields for any of these bodies. Perhaps a magnetic field is dependent upon the presence of molten or semi-molten layers in the interior of a planet. When we send probes to the other giant planets—Saturn, Uranus, Neptune—we may find that they have at least weak magnetic fields. If so, we would expect them to affect the solar wind in much the same way that earth and Jupiter do.

Earth's magnetic field (magnetosphere) traps subatomic particles of the solar wind, forming inner and outer belts (the Van Allen belts). A shock front is produced as the solar wind blows from the left. Particles trail the earth, producing a long, tapering tail that reaches far beyond the orbit of the moon.

Two cosmic particles are shown entering the upper atmosphere.

MAGNETIC FIELDS AND
COSMIC PARTICLES

The Russian probes Lunik I and II and numerous United States probes, including the Mariner series, had instruments aboard that measured the magnetic field of the solar wind. Once it was established that the wind is composed of ions, a magnetic field was known to exist; for one implies the other. The probes found that the field has a strength of a few hundred thousandths of a gauss. (A gauss is a unit of magnetic force. The magnetic field of the earth is about ½ gauss; that of the sun is 1 or 2 gauss.) Also, the probes found that the field does not radiate from the sun in straight (radial) lines, but rather in curved lines. But this was entirely as expected.

If the sun did not rotate (the equatorial region makes a turn in about twenty-six days), the magnetic lines of force would radiate straight out from the center. If a compass were held anywhere in that field, the needle must always point directly toward and away from the sun. But since the sun does rotate, the lines of force are curved. A compass needle held in them would point less and less toward the sun as distance from the sun increased. Basic laws of magnetism tell us that the strength of the magnetic field should decrease sharply with the increase of distance from the sun. At the distance of the earth (1 astronomical unit) the field should measure three or four hundred thousandths of a gauss. This figure was in keeping with the actual measurements made by the Russian and American space probes.

The energy producing the magnetic field of the solar wind comes from the sun, as indeed does the solar wind itself. The sun generates stupendous amounts of energy (all the energy of the earth, all of which it receives from the sun, for example,

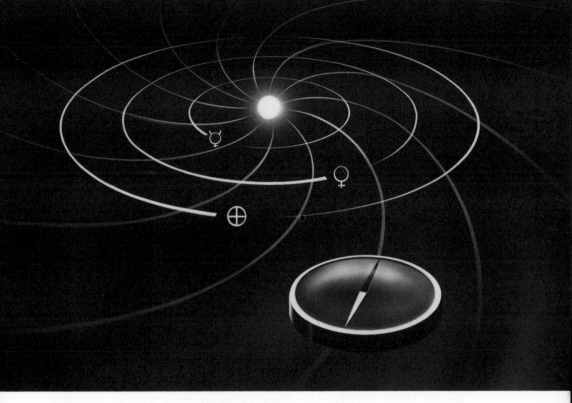

Because the sun rotates, magnetic lines of force are curved. As distance from the sun increases, a compass would point farther from the sun.

adds up to only one two-billionth of the sun's total). The sun's mass is equally impressive. We said earlier that each second the solar wind removes a million tons of hydrogen from the sun. That is a tremendous amount of matter. (A railroad coal car carries about 55 tons. So figure out how many cars you'd need each second to carry a million tons.) But the sun contains so much material that in 15 billion years, one million tons a second would amount to only about one hundredth of one percent (0.01%) of the total mass of the sun.

The solar wind is made of electrified particles (positive ions, or protons, for the most part) and it contains a magnetic field. Therefore, the solar wind must affect all other magnetic fields, and it must affect all other electrified particles—ions, either positive or negative. Cosmic particles are ions, and so they are affected by the solar wind. In fact, careful study of the cosmic particles, their abundance or scarcity, tells us a great deal about the extent of the solar wind. When there is intense solar activity, and the solar wind becomes gusty, the intensity of cosmic particles reaching the earth drops as much as 50 percent.

We know that solar activity varies in a cycle of about eleven years. That is, there might be intense activity for a few months, then a drop off to a low after about five years. Then activity would increase, reaching another peak in about eleven years from the start of the cycle.

Cosmic particles vary in the opposite fashion. When the sun is active, cosmic particle frequency is low and the cycle of cosmic particle activity goes along step by step inversely with the cycle of solar activity. But there is a steady, consistent lag of about six months. Suppose there was a drop in solar activity in January. In June there would be a marked increase in strength and frequency of cosmic particles. The lag must be due to the extent of the solar wind, because cosmic particles would be affected just as soon as they encountered the solar wind, wherever that might be. From January to June the decrease in solar wind intensity was traveling outward from the sun, like a ripple in a lake. When the decreased solar wind reached the "barrier" region where cosmic particles are admitted freely or robbed of some of their energy, the cosmic particles were let through. They reached the earth soon after.

We know that the solar wind moves very fast, covering an astronomical unit in just about four days. This means that in six months the solar wind would cover 40 or 50 astronomical units. According to this way of figuring, that would be the extent of the solar wind. But remember that according to measurements of density and magnetic fields, the solar wind

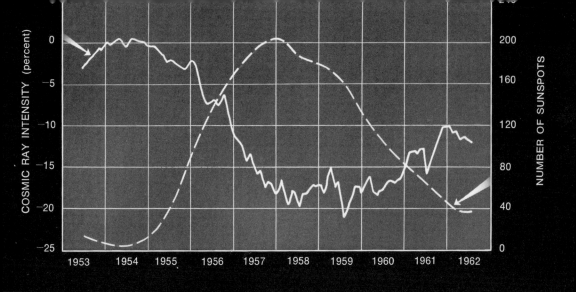

When the sun is especially active, clouds of charged particles are ejected. Shortly afterward, cosmic ray activity drops. Perhaps these clouds shield earth from cosmic particles that originate beyond the solar system.

might go as far as 160 AU into space. The extent of the solar wind is just one of the many things we hope to find out about the solar wind as research continues.

We'd like to know if other stars have a solar wind; if they have coronas that extend millions of miles into space. Chances are many of them do. There are millions of stars in our galaxy that are similar to our sun in many respects. It is reasonable to suppose that such stars support solar winds, even though we have no way presently of detecting their presence.

One possible way of getting some clues is through study of cosmic particles. These are ions that enter into the solar system from deep outer space. Perhaps some of them have passed through solar winds of other stars and bear an imprint of the experience. Presently no magic key has been found to unfold the stories cosmic particles may be able to tell. In the next chapter, however, we explain some of the information that we have about these cosmic "bullets," some of which contain millions of times as much energy as man has ever been able to pack into such a tiny bit of matter.

Cosmic Rays | 8

Every second of the day and night, billions of cosmic particles enter earth's atmosphere. They collide with atoms and produce billions of secondary particles. Every second, thousands of these secondary particles strike you, go right through you, and emerge again. It's a good thing they are invisible.

Fortunately we are not aware of cosmic particles. And for the most part they don't affect us at all. However, we know that they can cause slight changes in cell structure, which in turn might cause hereditary changes: mutations. Flowers that grow at high altitudes (where cosmic bombardment is energetic) show more mutations than would be expected to occur at lower elevations. Occasionally, cosmic particles must strike cells in higher forms of life and so initiate mutations. So it is reasonable to say that cosmic particles affect you and me in this way. Some people argue that the particles might also induce certain kinds of cancer in higher animals. The suggestion is not unreasonable.

Actually, our knowledge about cosmic particles is limited,

and it is all very new, for the nature of cosmic particles was not discovered until the early part of this century.

Toward the end of the last century, studies of radiation were made by Marie Curie, Henri Bequerel, and others. The radiation was energy given off by radioactive substances. One way of noting the presence of radiation is to expose an electroscope. If the electroscope becomes discharged, then particles must be striking it.

In principle the electroscope is simply a glass jar in which a cork is placed. A metal rod extends through the cork from outside the jar to the inside. The rod is bent so that a piece of gold foil can be hung over it. When a rubber comb that has been stroked on wool is brought near the wire, the foil is charged with ions. Since both leaves of the foil are charged, they stand apart, because like charges repel.

If the charge remained on the foil strips they would continue to stand apart, but they do not. Gradually the charge escapes, and the leaves come together. The charge escapes rapidly if the electroscope is near a source of radiation, uranium ore, for example.

In the early days of this century men did not understand why this happened. They knew that the electrons could move from the gold foil strips only if there were electrified atoms (ions) in the atmosphere to which they could go. Indeed, they found that the electroscope would hold the charge much longer if it were placed in a lead box, one that insulated the electroscope from the atmosphere and from the products of radiation from earth's surface. They surmised that radiation in the earth's crust was the factor that affected the electroscope. Here was something that could be tested quite easily. If the radiation causing discharge was from the earth's crust, it should become less with an increase in altitude.

In 1910, an electroscope was carried to the top of the

Eiffel Tower in Paris, and in 1912 another one was taken up in a balloon. There was a decrease; the leaves discharged more slowly, but not nearly as slowly as was expected.

The question was far from solved. But later that year, on August 7, 1912, cosmic rays were discovered and men knew why the electroscope discharged. On that day Victor F. Hess, an Austrian scientist, made a 2½-hour flight in a balloon with two

When an electroscope is charged, the leaves stand apart. Gradually, the charge escapes and the leaves collapse.

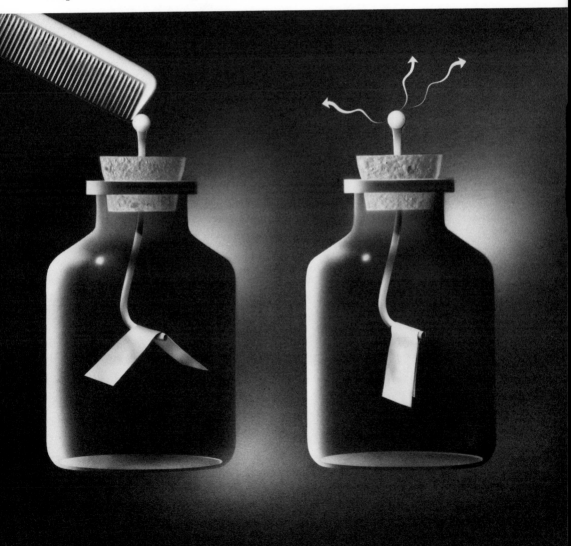

companions. They drifted to 16,000 feet. The electroscope they carried with them discharged faster as their altitude increased. The radiation-causing discharge was not coming from the surface of the earth, it was coming from beyond the earth. As Hess said, "The results of my observations are best explained by the assumption that a radiation of very great penetrating power enters our atmosphere from above."

Later on, further proof was found that Hess was correct. American researchers fitted electroscopes into watertight boxes and lowered them into a lake. The deeper the instruments went, the slower they discharged. Whatever caused the discharge must come from beyond the earth, not from within it.

Hess established that the radiation was coming from beyond the earth. But he did not know what cosmic particles actually were. In fact, the particles were not yet named. They were first called cosmic rays by Robert A. Millikan, one of the American scientists who performed the "lake" experiment mentioned above. He reasoned that the radiation came from beyond the earth, somewhere in the cosmos, so "cosmic particles" seemed appropriate.

It was found subsequently that the intensity of cosmic particles does not increase continually with increase in altitude. In a typical study it was found that at 10,000 feet intensity is 4 times what it is at sea level. At 25,000 feet the intensity was 30 times as great, and at 60,000 feet it was 100 times as great. However, at 100,000 feet the intensity dropped below the mark attained at 60,000 feet.

At first this was a baffling observation. It seemed to indicate that cosmic rays originate at an elevation of 60,000 feet above sea level. But when the particles themselves were studied, scientists found that the rays at 100,000 feet were made up of primary cosmic particles. Those at lower elevations were more numerous because they were secondary particles, objects produced when primary particles bombarded atoms and molecules in the air. Since at 100,000 feet the pressure of the air is only one percent of what it is at sea level, there is very little air, and so few collisions. At lower altitudes where the air is more dense, it would be rare for a cosmic particle to avoid a collision. Primary cosmic particles, those that exist outside our atmosphere, are mostly high-speed protons. A proton is a nucleus of a hydrogen atom. Protons are believed to be the basic material of the universe. The next most abundant particles are alpha particles—these are the nuclei of helium atoms—one step up the ladder of complexity beyond hydrogen. About one percent of cosmic particles are the nuclei of heavier atoms, all the way up to iron. The abundance and distribution of elements in cosmic particles is about the same as the distribution of elements in the universe as a whole. There are exceptions; lithium, beryllium, and boron are thousands of times more abundant in cosmic rays than they are in stars. This may be because these elements break down when exposed to high temperatures, such as those that exist in stars.

When primary particles enter earth's atmosphere, they collide with atoms and molecules. Depending upon the energy of the primary, the nuclei of molecules in the air are broken into smaller particles. The energy contained in the primary is transmitted to these secondary particles. When there is high activity, a shower of secondary particles is produced. Practically all of the cosmic particles experienced at sea level are secondary, the products of collisions in the upper atmosphere.

Our knowledge of cosmic particles increased tremendously in the end of the 1960's when satellites with sensitive counters were rocketed to high altitudes. These flights were the culmination of studies made in the 1940's and 1950's when rockoons (rockets carried aloft by balloons and fired at elevations of 15 miles) carried instruments some 60 or 70 miles above the earth.

The rockets were gathering information that would enable scientists to map the amount of cosmic radiation at high altitudes.

While gathering information near the north magnetic pole of the earth, the scientists found that the map of cosmic particles was developing about as expected. However, two flights in 1953 gave readings much higher than the others. James Van Allen, the researcher in charge, surmised that something was wrong with the equipment, and so it was checked. However, everything was working properly. Van Allen concluded that something new had been discovered. But no one knew what it was.

More rockoons were launched. They found X-rays and high-energy electrons. Furthermore, the radiation was found in both the northern and southern hemispheres. It was made up of protons as well as electrons, and it seemed to be concentrated in the regions where the auroras occurred—the northern lights (aurora borealis) and the southern lights (aurora australis). However, additional flights revealed that the radiation existed even when there were no auroral displays.

The observations could not be explained. The reason for the high-intensity radiation was not found until 1958 when the United States put Explorer I into orbit. Van Allen had instruments aboard the satellite to measure cosmic radiation and transmitters to send the information back to the earth. The findings were amazing. This early satellite of the Space Age revealed that the earth is surrounded by regions occupied by high-energy particles. It revealed the magnetosphere which surrounds the earth and which traps and retains radiation particles.

Explorer II went almost 1,600 miles above the earth. The information sent back was about as expected. However, when the highest elevation was reached over the equator, the reading dropped. Van Allen said it appeared that cosmic rays do not strike the upper layers of the atmosphere over the tropics. It was hard to accept such an explanation, for there seemed to be no reason for it.

Later that year Explorer III was launched. When it was over the tropics at an elevation of 200 to 300 miles, the radiation level dropped. But when Explorer was over the same region at an elevation of 500 to 600 miles, the level went up rapidly—and then it stopped altogether.

Van Allen and his group puzzled over this finding. They could not understand why the instruments suddenly stopped. He prevailed on the government to send up an Explorer with a path that would take it farther from the equator. Some people suggested they needed instruments that could measure higher levels of radiation. Maybe the other instruments jammed, they said. So Explorer IV had instruments aboard that could measure radiation particles far beyond those anticipated earlier.

The instruments worked. They showed very high levels of radiation. As Explorer moved in its orbit, the signals coming back to earth indicated there was a pattern to the radiation. The earth was surrounded by belts of radiation (the Van Allen belts). They are made up of particles (electrons partly) that spiral back and forth from the north magnetic pole to the south magnetic pole, moving along magnetic lines of force. The earth is a magnet and lines of force surround it, just as lines of force surround a bar magnet and can be revealed by iron filings. Explorer satellites had penetrated into these belts, regions no one had known about.

Further investigation of the belts since these early discoveries revealed that the earth's magnetic field extends some 60,000 miles into space. The Van Allen belts (it may be that there is a single belt with regions that vary in radiation level) extend some 14,000 miles beyond the earth's surface. The inner intense layer is about 500 to 4,500 miles above the surface. The level drops off until the outer intense region is reached some 10,000 miles from the earth. The thickness of this region is about 5,000 miles.

The outer region of the belts does not have sharp boundaries. Also, the shape of the belts changes, probably as a result of solar activity. The particles in the outer part of the Van Allen belts probably were originally part of the solar wind. The particles in the inner dense region may result from deterioration of solar wind components.

In the inner region the energy ranges up to 100 million electron volts, while in the outer area the energy is only a few million electron volts.

In expressing the energy levels of radiation particles, the electron volt is used. It is a very small amount of energy, being the energy acquired by an electron when it is accelerated by a potential difference of one volt. For example, a 20,000 volt television tube gives electrons 20,000 eV of energy. Cosmic rays possess fantastic amounts of energy. Most primary particles have energy in the order of 10^9 eV (a billion electron volts, or a Bev). However, some have energies of a billion, billion electron volts (10^{18} eV), or one billion Bev.

This may help you understand how much energy we're talking about. A high-energy cosmic particle has enough energy to lift a one-ounce weight to a height of one inch. That may not sound impressive, except that the weight of the particle itself is in the order of 0.000,000,000,000,000,000,000,000,060 of an ounce.

The gigantic energy of cosmic particles is astounding. And one of the challenges of science is to explain how these sub-atomic bits obtain the energy they possess. Where do the cosmic rays come from?

No one has the answer. Probably some of the particles come

from the sun. But that explanation cannot tell the whole story, for cosmic-ray activity is high at night when the earth is turned away from the sun. Currently scientists believe that most cosmic particles originate in explosions of stars. About once

Cosmic particles may have originated at the time of the creation of the universe. They may abound in the galactic halo, space beyond the galaxy, spiraling along magnetic lines of force.

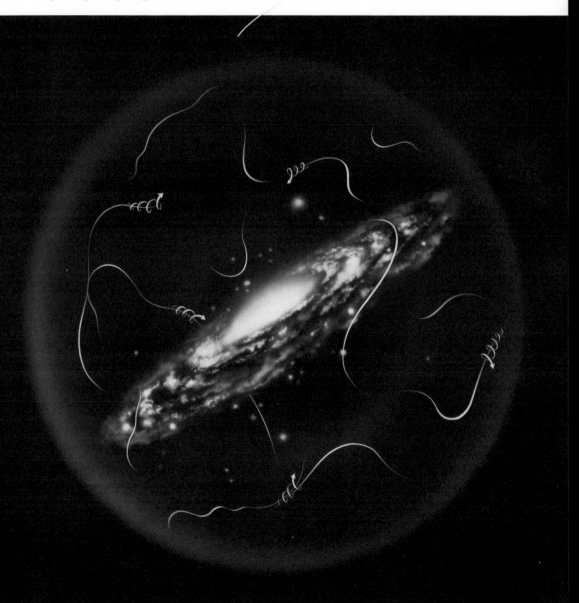

every century a star in our galaxy explodes, releasing stupendous amounts of energetic particles. The particles are trapped within the galaxy by its magnetic field. It has been said that the magnetic field acts as a "magnetic bottle" which holds the cosmic particles. The particles fly through space, striking solid objects such as earth, and so they diminish in number. But each time there's a supernova, a star that rapidly increases its activity so it produces millions of times as much energy as it normally would, the supply is replenished.

Or, cosmic particles may have originated at the time of creation. They may be remnants of the cataclysm that produced the solar system, the stars, and the galaxy.

Comets, asteroids, and meteoroids are mavericks of the solar system. Perhaps cosmic rays should be called mavericks of the galaxy. While they abound in the space of the solar system, they must come into being far beyond, out among the stars. They are truly space wanderers.

Suggested Further Reading

Hawkins, Gerald. *Meteors, Comets and Meteorites,* 1964, McGraw-Hill, New York.

LaPaz, Lincoln. *Space Nomads,* 1961, Holiday House, New York.

Ley, Willy. *The Meteorite Craters,* 1968, Weybright and Talley, New York.

————. *Visitors from Afar,* 1969, McGraw-Hill, New York.

Lyttleton, R. A. *The Comets and Their Origins,* 1953, Cambridge University Press, England.

Mason, Brian. *Meteorites,* 1962, John Wiley, New York.

Nininger, H. H. *Arizona's Meteorite Crater,* 1956, World Press, Inc., Denver.

Richardson, Robert J. *Getting Acquainted with the Comets,* 1967, McGraw-Hill, New York.

Watson, Fletcher G. *Between the Planets,* 1956, Harvard University Press, Cambridge, Mass.

Wood, John A. *Meteorites and the Origin of the Solar System,* 1968, McGraw-Hill, New York.

Index

About the Author

Franklyn M. Branley, Astronomer Emeritus and former Chairman of The American Museum–Hayden Planetarium, is the author of many books, pamphlets, and articles on various aspects of science for young readers. COMETS, METEOROIDS, AND ASTEROIDS is the seventh in the "Exploring Our Universe" series, written by Dr. Branley and illustrated by Helmut Wimmer.

Dr. Branley holds degrees from New York University, Columbia University, and the State University of New York College at New Paltz. He and his wife live in Woodcliff Lake, New Jersey, and spend their summers at Sag Harbor, New York.

About the Illustrator

Helmut Wimmer was born in Munich, Germany, and was apprenticed at the age of fourteen as a sculptor and architectural model-maker. After World War II he worked as a sculptor in the restoration of damaged buildings in Russia, where he had been a prisoner of war, and also in Germany. In 1954 Mr. Wimmer came to the United States and began a new career, as painter of astronomical subjects and Art Supervisor of The American Museum–Hayden Planetarium. His paintings have been exhibited in many cities around the United States, and have also appeared in *Graphis, Physics Today, Smithsonian Magazine, Natural History,* and many other magazines. With his wife and children, he lives in Bergenfield, New Jersey.